CW00420141

GARDEN UK

GARDEN UK

ROB CASSY

To Margaret Parry
The pearl of great price

First published in 2003 by
Conran Octopus Limited
a part of Octopus Publishing Group
2–4 Heron Quays, London E14 4JP

To order please ring Conran Octopus Direct
on 01903 828503

British Library Cataloguing-in-Publication Data.
A catalogue record for this book is available from
the British Library.

ISBN: 1 84091 329 0

Publishing Director: Lorraine Dickey
Senior Editor: Katey Day
Art Director: Chi Lam
Design: johnson banks
Picture Research: Rob Cassy and Anne-Marie Hoines
Production Manager: Angela Couchman

Printed in China

CONTENTS

INTRODUCTION

Gardening and shopping are twin passions of mine, and if you're reading these words then I imagine the same holds true for you. Combining these two pursuits, and in the name of work, has been an absolute joy. In my travels around the UK I've come across lots of very talented artists and craftspeople, and I've found some really gorgeous shops, all of them offering exciting products and services to enhance the outdoor space. Some of them I've known, or known about, for years. Others were as new to me as I hope they are to you. What all of them have in common is excellence.

If a shop is listed here it has a good range of well-chosen stock, it is attractively laid-out, the staff are helpful and knowledgeable.

If a maker is listed, be they carpenter or sculptor, blacksmith or potter, then they are either a well-established leader in their field or a wildly innovative newcomer. There are names that are already recognised throughout the world, there are names about to enter that league.

Above all else, shops and suppliers in *Garden UK* are friendly and welcoming. Makers are not only approachable, they will listen to your ideas and then help make your dreams come true in ways you could never have imagined.

All the people I've visited work incredibly hard. They have to make hay while the sun shines because garden retailing, like gardening itself, is a seasonal business. This means that they will sometimes close their doors for a day or so at peak times to seek out a wider market for their wares at flower shows, county fairs, or at specialist exhibitions. Over the notoriously slow winter months some take a well-deserved break. If you're planning on travelling any great distance to pay a special call, whatever the time of year, it's a good idea to telephone ahead and make sure that there'll be someone there to greet you.

My simple aim in writing this book has been to bring these people's efforts to as wide and appreciative an audience as possible. Surprisingly, although there are some excellent directories on tracking down plants and seeds, and there are countless gazetteers listing gardens open to the public, there has never before been a guide to things for the garden. So *Garden UK* is something of an adventure. And it's one I want you to join me on. I would like future editions to include readers' comments on the companies I've listed, and because gardeners are a generous bunch, I'm sure that many of you will want to share special shops of your own with the rest of us. Drop me a line or e-mail me. I'm ready and waiting to sort through your notes, and I can't wait to pack my bags and to set off again in search of the very best of British.

Rob Cassy
rob@robcassy.com

Icons
These icons will enable you to see at a glance which products are stocked in each store and the specialist areas of each shop or maker.

Furniture

Lighting

Ornaments & Sculpture

Water Features

Structures

Hard Landscaping

Bespoke

Tools & Equipment

South-east England

South-west England & Wales

Midlands

North England & Northern Ireland

Scotland

COLUMBIA ROAD JARDINIQU
THE MODERN GARDEN COMPA
PURVES & PURVES HOLLOWA
CRANBORNE ANTIQUES MICH
WHICHFORD POTTERY GARDE
THE WADHAM TRADING COM
RICHARD CHARTERS HEALS
POTS AND PITHOI BELINDA EA
GAZE BURVILL THE HANNAH
STAPELEY WATER GARDENS
ANTHONY DE GREY TRELLISES
NATURAL DRIFTWOOD SCULP
WILLIAM PYE JUDY GREENE'S

THE IRON DESIGN COMPANY
NY GARDEN ART HAVENPLAN
S MARSTON AND LANGINGER
AEL HILL GALLOWAY GRANITE
IMAGES CLIFTON NURSERIES

ANY **SHOPS & SUPPLIERS** CED

EAR TREE THE CONRAN SHOP
DE MARK PEDRO DE LA TORRE
ESCHAR SCULPTURE GARDEN
PLANTS OF SPECIAL INTEREST
R K ALLISTON LEISURE PLAN
URES GARDEN ARCHITECTURE
GARDEN STORE LOUISE KERR

It is of course inevitable that the densely populated south-east of England, with the great metropolis of London buzzing at its economic core, should be incredibly well endowed with gardening riches. Designers, manufacturers and retailers – not to mention all the artists, artisans and technicians – aren't just catering to the home market, many are selling the UK to the rest of the world. Not only should we all be incredibly proud of this, its something we can all benefit from. Market forces ensure that the greater choice we have as consumers, the better the goods and the services we are offered.

It is a truth universally acknowledged that gardens close to the capital, though the houses cost a fortune, are in want of more space. Statistics from the National Census show that there are more flat dwellers in this region than in any other part of the country, and a balcony or a roof terrace is a much sought-after luxury. The end result of all this is that potted plants, ornaments and sculpture have to take the place of ample lawns and generously filled beds and borders.

Every square metre of outdoor space here is precious and must be enjoyed to the full, all year round. So feast your eyes now on antiques and mosaics, sundials and water features, contemporary furniture and stunning containers.

SOUTH-EAST ENGLAND

ANDREW CRACE

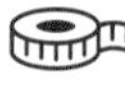

PRODUCTS INCLUDE:
Bamboo cloches
Bamboo wigwams
Benches & chairs
Bronze statues and water features
Garden signs
Labelling equipment
Parasols
Plant tags
Stone lanterns
Sun loungers
Swing seats
Tables
Topiary frames

Andrew Crace
Bourne Lane
Much Hadham
Hertfordshire
SG10 6ER
01279 842 685
www.andrewcrace.com
Open: Mon – Fri 10 – 4
Other times by appointment

Though he sells many more things besides as you'll see from the list, permanent plant tags, bronze statuary and distinctive wooden furniture are the three lines most associated with Andrew Crace. His own most demanding customer, he went into production because as a gardener and designer himself he couldn't find work of the quality he required.

His discreet aluminium plant tags come in two grades which are in private and institutional use the whole world over. Both kinds are reusable if written on with pencil; the professional grade can be permanently name-stamped using a series of punches with a steel and brass jig. There is a popular range of copper tags and ties which can be embossed with a ball-point pen, and for a less formal look there are tags in teak and bamboo too.

Ancient and classical figures feature heavily in the bronze collection: there are life-size studies of wild and domesticated animals and, for a little bit of fun, stylized spouting frogs in a variety of poses. Where many garden seats on the market are either (a) attractive or (b) comfortable, Andrew Crace's are (c) both of the above. He is only happy with his designs when looks and utility come together as one. After scouring pattern books and scrutinizing Victorian and Edwardian photographs for inspiration, early prototypes were tested out in the family home first and only got the go-ahead if they were comfortable as kitchen chairs in daily use. There are now around a hundred different pieces in the range and it is a real testimony to their stylish lines and the quality of workmanship that the furniture is as sought after by interior designers, and bodies like English Heritage and the National Trust, as by professional garden designers and gardening enthusiasts in the know. The Lutyens throne so beloved of English gardens has been reinterpreted with a contoured seat instead of the numbingly flat one of the originals. The Indian, Chinoiserie and Edo sun loungers adjust to three different positions and have a movable side tray for drinks and books. The elegant Boscobel seat has intriguingly stepped arm-rests which turn out, when you sit down, to accommodate elbow and wrist to perfection. Special gems include glorious swing benches for decadent lolling and wheelbarrow seats for chasing the sun or for seeking out shade. If you can't visit to try them yourself, then a catalogue is available on request.

ANTHONY DE GREY TRELLISES

PRODUCTS INCLUDE:
Arbour seats
Archways
Decking
Gazebos
Pavilions
Planters
Rose arches
Trellising

Anthony de Grey Trellises
Broadhinton Yard
77a North Street
London
SW4 0HQ
020 7738 8866
www.anthonydegrey.com
Showroom viewing by appointment

If you think that trellising is just for training the odd clematis up a wall or raising the height of a fence, then you need to see the work of landscape gardener Anthony de Grey. For almost three decades now, Anthony and his team of craftsmen have been the specialist creators of custom-built trelliswork, and their services are eagerly sought both by garden designers in the know and by private individuals who have admired the company's memorable award-winning stands at the Chelsea Flower Show.

Treillage is wonderful for relieving the tedium of urban courtyards by introducing strong decorative elements. It can effectively block out ugly views, embarrassingly near neighbours and inquisitive passers-by while keeping light loss to a minimum. Archways present the opportunity to make an impressive entrance to a garden or to mark the transition from one area to another. In confined areas, *trompe l'oeil* archways with receding perspectives can introduce a much needed feeling of depth. Perhaps the most overlooked use for trellising though lies in selectively framing the available view to make the very most of your surroundings – a cutaway arch or porthole can focus the eye on a distant object of beauty while the trelliswork itself blanks out horrors closer to home.

Anthony de Grey offers a complete design-and-build service from his London office and has a nearby showroom where clients can view samples of his work. Panels can be any height or width. They can be flat-topped, softly swagged, gently arched or shaped like soaring great Gothic windows. Latticing can run vertically and horizontally in squares, or diagonally to create diamonds. Cutaways can be square or circular, like arched windows or like doorways. There's a choice of decorative finials for supporting posts, and colour contrast between trelliswork and background can be used to dramatic effect. Archways can alternate with checkerboard-type flat-topped ones – with or without cut-outs. The permutations and combinations are endless. What is more, the end result is gorgeous all year round. Unlike that clematis.

BELINDA EADE

PRODUCTS INCLUDE:
Chandeliers
Fountains
Grottoes
Inscriptions
Plaques
Relief carvings

Belinda Eade
Studio 70
Great Western Studios
The Lost Goods Building
Great Western Road
London
W9 3NY
020 7266 0328
www.belindaeade.com
Works to commission

Designing and building grottoes is a passion for Belinda Eade. No wonder. Cool, dark, sometimes damp and always mysterious, they are beautiful, magical, enchanting places. A welcoming physical retreat from the glare of the sun on a scorching summer's day, a grotto is also a spiritual and emotional bolt-hole. Entering is an invitation to another world; leaving is a form of rebirth. There's night and day, life and death, good and evil, the conscious and the unconscious – opposites of all kinds will provoke and tantalize the mind as you come and as you go. If garden design is about changing perspectives then installing a grotto is an eye-opener indeed.

The dualistic nature of a grotto extends to its construction. It is sheer artifice of course, and hard work too, but it has to look as old as the hills and as though formed, if not quite by nature alone, certainly not by the hand of man. Though structural engineers and builders may be employed by Belinda in the early stages of her work, the elfin-work encrustations of seashells and stone depend entirely on her artist's vision and jeweller's touch.

Belinda studied jewellery design at the Edinburgh School of Art then at the Central School of Art and Design in London. On graduation she was invited to join Diana Reynell – her former tutor at Marlborough College – and sculptor Simon Verity in grotto restoration at Painshill Park and Hampton Court. After being involved at Leeds Castle on the creation of an entirely new grotto and then honing her stone-carving skills at New York's Cathedral of St John the Divine and hewing out giant mantelpieces in a Scottish manse, her career path was truly established.

Besides building entire grottoes, Belinda has created wall reliefs, fountains, plaques and even chandeliers in the grotto style – so a little piece of magic and madness could always be yours. Her studio also designs and carves inscriptions for all kinds of stonework.

Belinda has many sources for her shells, including friendly local restaurants and fishmongers. If you fancy trying your hand at a little shellwork of your own, but don't have a ready supply of raw materials, a mail-order service is available from Eaton's Seashells, 020 8539 5288, www.eatonsseashells.co.uk.

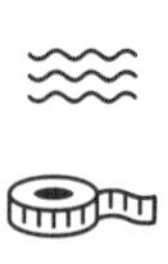

PRODUCTS INCLUDE:
Balls
Birdbaths
Cisterns
Finials
Fountains
Planters
Statuary
Urns
Wall plaques
Water tanks
Window boxes

Bulbeck Foundry
Reach Road
Burwell
Cambridgeshire
CB5 0AH
01638 743 153
www.bulbeckfoundry.co.uk
Open: Mon – Fri 8.30 – 5.30
(Please telephone beforehand)

'There can scarcely be a doubt that the happiest material for our garden sculpture and ornament is lead.' So said Gertrude Jekyll, the undisputed grande dame of English gardening. Who would dare to argue? More to the point, who would dream of arguing?

Lead is a soft, bluish-grey metal that acquires a mellow chalky white patina, or oxide layer, in the presence of air and moisture. It tones well with green foliage, it contrasts beautifully with flowers, it throws brickwork into relief and blends perfectly with stone. Where bronze can sometimes seem too opulent and steel too clinical, there's a grainy organic quality inherent to lead that makes it blend with the surrounding landscape.

Founded in 1988, the Bulbeck Foundry has slowly but surely expanded its range of statues, birdbaths and elaborate tiered fountains, many of which are direct copies taken from seventeenth-, eighteenth- and nineteenth-century antiques. Planters and water tanks come in standard sizes but can also be made to almost any proportions you choose, and coats of arms, crests, initials and dates can be added as required. Furthermore, experienced craftsmen can restore ailing and damaged leadwork of any variety to its former glory.

The decorative lead cisterns can be used as practical water butts to collect rainwater from rooftops, or they can be operated as self-contained water features, with lions or classical human heads or a decorative back panel constantly recirculating water from the tank beneath. Most dramatic of all perhaps is the multispout cistern based on the vast baroque cattle trough at Leonforte in Sicily, with cannon-like nozzles trickling mellifluously into the receptacle beneath.

Although there is no formal showroom, there is plenty to see if you're interested in buying, and staff are happy to advise both on items in stock and on special commissions.

CED

MATERIALS INCLUDE:
Aggregates
Basalt columns
Cobbles
Granite setts
Grotto rock
Mosaic setts
Paving slabs
Pebbles
Polished pebbles
Rockery stone
Spaghetti rock
Standing stones

PRODUCTS INCLUDE:
Carved animals
Drilled boulders
Footbridges
Japanese basins
Japanese lanterns
Mill wheels
Stepping stones
Stone troughs
Waterfall features

CED
728 London Road
West Thurrock
Grays
Essex
RM20 3LU
01708 867 237
www.ced.ltd.uk
Open: Mon – Fri 9 – 5

Scottish Depot
Allandale, nr Bonnybridge
01324 841 321

Midlands Depot
Langley Mill, Nottinghamshire
01773 769 916

Thames Valley Depot
West Drayton, Middlesex
01895 422 411

There's no disputing the simple beauty of natural stone. Sadly though, anything beyond the odd bag of gravel and the smallest of rockery stones can be difficult to source, so you rarely see this versatile medium achieving anything like its full potential in a garden setting. A visit to CED will really open your eyes.

CED has been supplying stone of all kinds and in all forms to trade and private buyers since 1978. It now has a total of four depots nationwide, the largest being at West Thurrock, its head-office site. Not only does the company have a vast range of stock to draw on, its knowledgeable staff can advise on all aspects of designing with stone and arrange for delivery to your door. Natural boulders and rough-hewn rocks up to 20 tonnes in weight are available for creating spectacular rockeries and waterfalls as well as for use as standing stones. These certainly will not be going home in the back of the car, but you will be tempted to test your suspension with the hand-carved lanterns for Japanese gardens and the modern geometric water features. Once you have made your choice you'll be only too keen to see them in situ.

Over the years, Managing Director Michael Heap has seen a rapid increase in the demand for natural stone and for paving in particular. Everyone's familiar with sawn or cleft York stone and slate of course, but what about Donegal quartzite or Caithness flags? Pennant or Purbeck or Portland? How about Indian sandstone in red or pink or beige or green, or limestone in blue or black? Granite setts can be flame textured, bush hammered or polished; the stone itself can be from France, Portugal or China, and it comes in shades ranging from silvery grey to black and in all sorts of hues. Most beautiful of all perhaps are the setts of Italian porphyry, a hard igneous rock shading from brown through red to purple and grey. The rich tapestry-like effect they create when laid is positively breathtaking. Then again, if formality's your thing CED's Czech mosaic setts in white or grey marble, green syenite or beige limestone look decidedly dapper when laid out in patterns. If you're after something that's already aged and weathered, CED maintains good stocks of reclaimed materials too.

CLIFTON NURSERIES

Clifton Nurseries
5a Clifton Villas
Little Venice
London
W9 2PH
020 7289 6851
www.clifton.co.uk
Open: Mon – Sat 8.30 – 5.30 (winter)
Mon – Sat 8.30 – 6.00 (summer)
Sun 10.30 – 4.30

If you want a complete revamp, Clifton's in-house specialists offer services including garden design, landscaping, and the installation of garden structures and lighting. Gardeners may come and gardeners may go, but there's been a horticultural business on this intriguing site since the 1860s, making Clifton the capital's oldest established nursery. Unlike other places I could mention, it's genuinely grand without being in the least bit conceited, and for gardening *aficionados* visiting London for the first time it ranks alongside Kew Gardens, the Chelsea Physic Garden and Columbia Road Market as a must-see destination. You mightn't even be able to carry anything back with you, but memories of how much can be achieved in so constrained a space will make you green with envy on your return home, especially when you consider what's on offer at your average local garden centre.

Aside from all the conventional modes of transport, a lovely way of getting here is by canal boat either from Regent's Park or from the lock at Camden Market. Living well up to its name, Little Venice is awash with water and bridges, and beware, as it's all too easy to lose your bearings and get hopelessly lost. If you haven't found the nurseries within a very few minutes of arrival, buttonhole a local or you'll overshoot the mark.

Once down the arched alleyway between some elegant stuccoed houses, you'll think you've died and gone to heaven. For starters there's a florist's shed spilling over with fantastic cut flowers and a shop selling useful tools, sundries, gardening gifts and greetings cards. Then there's the great selection of large, unusual 'specimen' plants as well as a wide range of annuals, perennials, shrubs and climbers. The conservatory holds what has to be the most extensive stock of tropical plants in London, and it also houses a really stylish collection of vases and cachepots and pots in all kinds of materials for indoors and out. The modern Domani-brand zinc planters are perfect for balconies and roof gardens; they look heavy and imposing yet are incredibly lightweight thanks to their double-skin construction. There are cast-stone planters and statuary too, and there's also the Clifton Little Venice handmade wooden furniture inspired by eighteenth- and nineteenth-century pattern books.

Clifton's in-house specialists offer garden design, landscaping and maintenance services that are second to none. A passion for design is truly at the fore here. Not only has the nursery won five gold medals at the Chelsea Flower Show, it has a commendable history of commissioning its own buildings from such award-winning architects as Jeremy Dixon, Terry Farrell and Harper Mackay Ltd. And who knows what you might find here when you visit in future...

PRODUCTS INCLUDE:
Antique ornaments
Bespoke wooden furniture
Cachepots
Cut flowers
Plants
Pots & planters
Statuary
Tools
Vases
Wirework

COLUMBIA ROAD MARKET

Columbia Road Market
Columbia Road
London
E2
www.columbia-flower-market.freewebspace.com
Open: Sun 7–2

Apart from snuggling up with a loved one or propping yourself up in bed to read the papers, there isn't a great deal of entertainment in London first thing on a Sunday morning. Unless you're a gardener and a shopper, that is. In which case you might like to join your fellow enthusiasts who descend in their hordes each week on this little patch of paradise in the heart of the East End.

The great joy of the place is that you never know quite what you'll come across, so go with an open mind and a safely stashed walletful of ready money. Over the course of a year you'll find every garden plant and cut flower from acer to zinnia being cried from the tightly packed stalls lining the street, all in the peak of condition, and at prices so low you'll hardly believe your own ears. Huge exotics for the home and for the

PRODUCTS INCLUDE:
Antiques
Bulbs
Cut flowers
Furniture
Glassware
Plants
Pots & planters
Statuary
Tinware
Tools
Trees
Water features
Wirework
Zinc planters

conservatory are quite commonplace here, and plantsmen and plantswomen accustomed to tracking down their rarities through the *RHS Plantfinder* will be amazed at the selection of really choice outdoor specimens on offer in one or two of the lock-ups.

Plants are only part of the Columbia Road story. In the shops along the narrow pavement on the south side you'll find Moroccan garden furniture, handsome old tools, pots ancient and modern, glassware, garden designers, perfumiers, some serious antiques and some very frivolous vintage clothing. And if all that weren't enough, there's more to discover in the courtyards and passageways to the north, including a family-run pottery full of planters and tree ferns, and some excellent bric-a-brac dealers. You will soon find your own favourites among the hustle and bustle, but at the top of my list are Putnams in Ezra Courtyard and Open House at 152 Columbia Road, both of which have beautifully chosen country antiques and gardenalia.

For sustenance there are bagels, seafood and coffee aplenty, and when you keel over at lunchtime under the weight of your purchases there are several good pubs where you can pause for rest and recuperation before snapping a few last-minute bargains knocked down to clear as trading draws to a close.

If you live in London you'll probably go straight home with your goodies. If you're a visitor you'll have feasted your eyes but you'll be travelling light, so you can now choose to make your way to the west by bus or tube where all the galleries and museums will be opening their doors for the afternoon.

THE CONRAN SHOP

PRODUCTS INCLUDE:
Barbecues
Bell cloches
Candles & flares
Conservatory furniture
Funky hand tools
Outdoor seating
Parasols
Patio heaters
Plant stands
Pots & planters
Wall lights

The Conran Shop
Michelin House
81 Fulham Road
London
SW3 6RD
020 7589 7401
www.conran.com
Open: Mon, Tue, Fri 10–6
Wed, Thu 10–7
Sat 10–6.30
Sun 12–6

Terence Conran's retailing career began in 1964 when he opened the first Habitat on Fulham Road. The store became a lifestyle phenomenon and quickly grew into an international chain. Frustrated at finding products that were too expensive, too esoteric or in too short a supply for the Habitat range, a desire was nurtured to '... create an individual store where really beautiful things were sold, where people could expect to find the *crème de la crème* of design...' When the original Habitat relocated to premises on the King's Road in 1973, dreams turned into reality, the site was redeveloped and The Conran Shop was born.

While Habitat is now owned by IKEA, The Conran Shop remains in its founder's hands. It moved to the enormous Michelin House with its striking Art Deco façade in 1987 and now has branches in London, Paris, New York and Japan.

Conran Shop buyers travel the world to source new and exciting objects, often developing exclusive product lines in association with designers and manufacturers. As you walk in off the street, straight into the outdoor living department, all that creativity shows. The glass bell cloches are the sleekest you'll find. Amoeba-shaped Blob planters bring bounce back to zinc. The dynamic lines of architect Rodolfo Dordoni's heavyweight Ming planter in recycled polyethylene are such that you'd be tempted to leave it empty as a purely sculptural piece. The polished terrazzo benches are so striking that you'd have them indoors if your floorboards could take the strain, while the seagrass sofas and chairs for conservatory use could be carried outdoors in an instant on a summery day. There are serious barbecues for serious cook-outs and nifty little fish-shaped ones for *diner à deux* that double as food-warmers. You can eat lunch around a table in the shade of a giant parasol, then you can keep dinner guests talking long into the night in the comfortable glow of a sleek continental-style gas heater. Traditional quality blends with contemporary styling. Looks and practicality come together. The outdoors merges with the indoors as the contemporary garden becomes another room of the home. Mesh Man wire furniture could as easily be sold from the home furnishings department; Philippe Starck's colourful Toy armchair in air-moulded polypropylene and his transparent polycarbonate La Marie side chair could as easily be sold from outdoor living. Confused? You won't be. Just delighted at this outstanding outdoor lifestyle phenomenon.

London branches: 55 Marylebone High Street, W1, 020 7723 2223. 12 Conduit Street, W1, 020 7399 0710. 350 King's Road, SW3, 020 7559 1140

CRANBOURNE
ANTIQUES

PRODUCTS INCLUDE:
Bulb planters
Clay spades
Double hoes
Fruit pickers
Garden lines
Hand lights
Hedge trimmers
Lawn edgers
Plant tags
Pruning saws
Riddles
Syringes
Terracotta pots
Watering cans
Wire frogs

Cranborne Antiques
Stand No 4a
113 Portobello Road
London
W11 2QB
07785 336 574
Open: Sat 7.30 – 2

Notting Hill, possibly London's most exciting area, is the haunt of pop-stars and politicians, film-stars and fashionistas, TV celebrities and media has-beens. The titled and the quietly well-off live next door to brash young *nouveaux-riches* in stucco-fronted terraces. Bed-sits and studios accommodate up-and-coming talent, the temporarily down-at-heel and the long-term down-at-heart; while ordinary flats and houses are home to a melting pot of cultures from all around the globe. At the crack of dawn each Saturday, residential 'Notting Hill' is magically transformed into commercial 'Portobello'; the rich and famous having left town for their country retreats, the streets now throng with incomers.

Portobello, too, is a multi-layered world: for the sightseer there is plain old tourist tat but if you know where to look, there is treasure. At first you see only hawkers, runners and a street market with stalls. Then you see the shops. But every now and again, a simple-looking doorway leads into an Aladdin's cave of an arcade filled with dealers whose fields range from ancient art to seventies retro, and whose expertise easily matches and often surpasses that of museum curators.

One such doorway is to be found at 113 Portobello Road, and the specialist that gardeners flock to, like bees round honey, is Deborah Cutler.

Deborah travels all around the UK and continental Europe to source her ever-changing stock, gleaning arcane horticultural knowledge along the way. Asparagus knives, strawberry baskets, florist's vases, bulb-sorters, fruit-picking cups, cucumber-straighteners and mistletoe-cutters are just some of the curiosities to catch your eye and to tempt your pocket. In case you're wondering, a mistletoe-cutter consists of a horizontal blade with an adjacent hook mounted on a long shaft – a sharp upward thrust detaches the white-berried parasite from its host tree of apple, hawthorn, lime or poplar and a concerted pull then brings it down to earth.

Each May, Cranborne Antiques takes a stand at the RHS Chelsea Flower Show, where the gardening world's *cognoscenti* vie for the cream of Deborah's annual crop – perhaps early nineteenth-century bell cloches turned mauve by the magnesium content of the glass, perhaps orchid stands designed to display these magnificent blooms to best effect. What is certain, there'll always be some choice botanical prints from the wide range Deborah carries throughout the year at stands 32a and 33a just across the aisle from her gardening bygones in Portobello.

Incidentally, that film really was shot in Notting Hill and Hugh Grant's bookshop, contrary to popular belief, was at 142 Portobello Road, then an antiques arcade itself, now the interior design shop Gong. I should know: as a minor footnote in cinematic history, the Open/Closed sign on his door was something that I ran off one night on a friend's computer and fastened together the next morning with garden twine.

THE CROOKED GARDEN

PRODUCTS INCLUDE:
Artificial flowers
Baskets & trugs
Bird feeders
Bridgewater pottery
Candle sconces
Cast-iron doormats
Country antiques
Enamelware
Fishing baskets
Hazel hurdles
Lanterns
Moroccan lanterns
Plant tags
Rusted-iron plant supports
Shaker-style birds
Sisal bags
Soaps & toiletries
Wall sconces
Watering cans
Wickerwork
Wirework
Zinc buckets & planters

The Crooked Garden
57 Tarrant Street
Arundel
West Sussex
BN18 9DJ
01903 885 133
Open: Wed – Sat 10.30 – 4.30

You know by the name alone what you're going to find here, and you know that you're going to like it. The crooked man in the nursery rhyme was undoubtedly the earliest recorded experiment of shabby chic and, though we aren't told for certain that he had a garden, I imagine that while the cat and mouse wore each other out running round the house, he filled it with old-fashioned annuals and perennials, allowed the best of the self-sown seedlings to stay so that the countryside would come right up to his back door, and that over the years he added all sorts of decorative bits and bobs picked up on his travels.

John and Annie Mash have always lived and gardened in the countryside, raising their children variously in East Anglia and in Herefordshire, always with a menagerie of animals in tow and a buzz of idealism and creativity in the air. The couple, who met at Chichester, both have a background in theatre, and John still writes plays for Radio 4. Son Julian is now a rock musician with his own record label in Brighton; daughter Holly is a newly qualified homeopathic vet. When the children flew the nest, the Mashes returned to their Sussex downland roots and bought a charming old three-storey house dating back to 1660 in the heart of historic Arundel. At first it was only meant to be a home, but the ground floor had once been a shop ... and it wasn't long before John and Annie's passion for collecting, love of gardening and skill at creating an atmosphere led to the opening of The Crooked Garden.

The quaint old shopfront painted eau-de-nil and cream forms the perfect backdrop to the pavement display of rusted iron plant frames and candle sconces (both English and Moroccan), hazel hurdles, wicker baskets and lovely sisal bags. Through the windows your eyes will light on Shaker-style birds, lanterns, teak plant tags and Bridgewater pottery. Inside you'll discover lovely old storage jars spilling over with old-fashioned wayside flowers such as Queen Anne's lace and forget-me-nots; there's cream and green enamelware; exquisite hats by milliner Gil Fox; there are sturdy zinc buckets and cast-iron doormats; there are sensible dispensers for string and perfectly balanced watering cans. The mix of the utilitarian and the purely ornamental is perfect. What's more, with John and Annie's regular trips to *brocanteurs* across the Channel where they buy as much for themselves as for the shop, there are always some really exquisite items from the past here – which magazine stylists often race down from London to borrow for shoots. Did I say earlier that you'd like this place? Like everyone else who comes time and again, you'll love it.

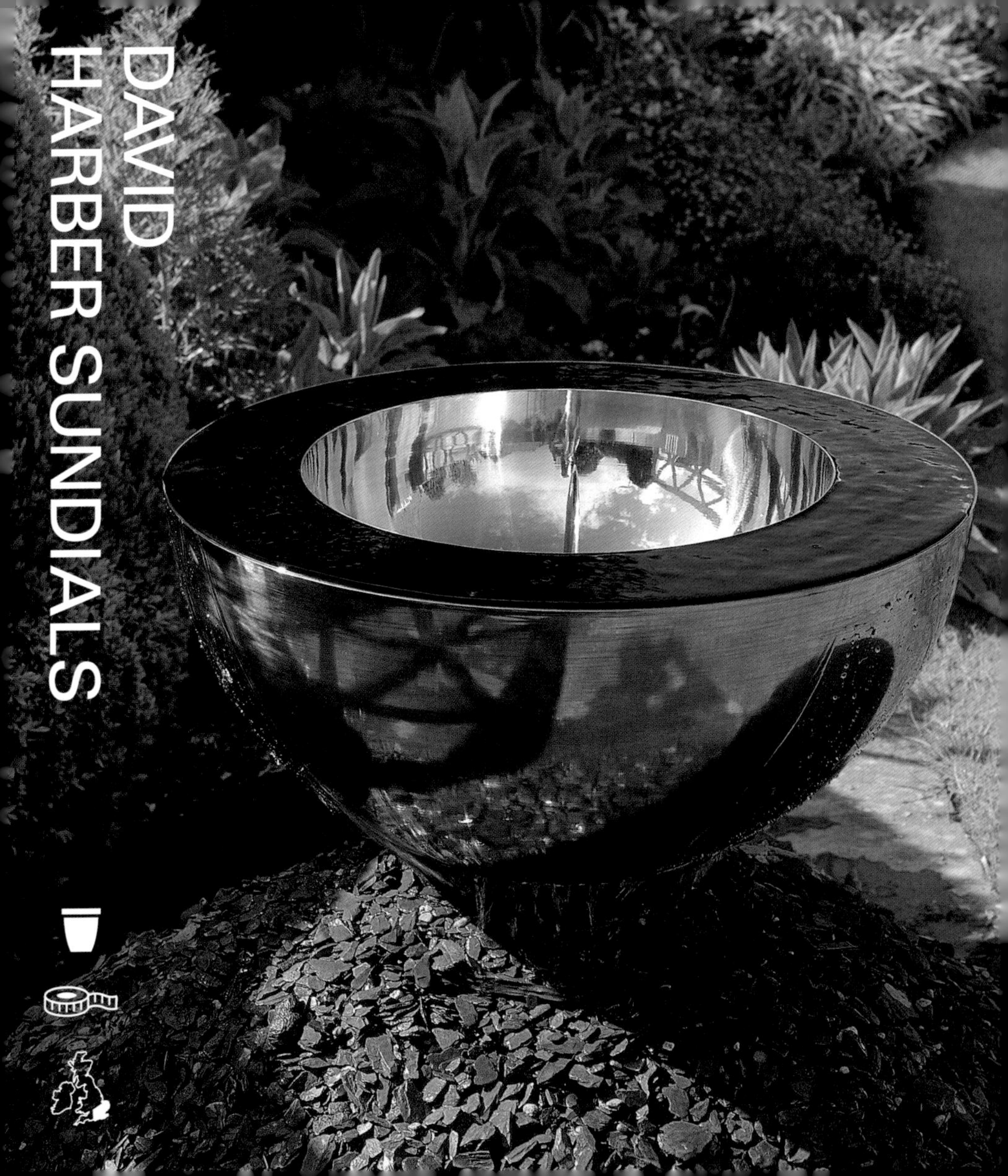
DAVID
HARBER SUNDIALS

PRODUCTS INCLUDE:
Armillary spheres
Cones
Horizontal dials
Monoliths
Obelisks
Rills
Vertical dials

David Harber Sundials
Valley Farm
Bix
Henley-on-Thames
Oxfordshire
RG9 6BW
01491 576 956
www.davidharbersundials.com
Works to commission

'Come! Light! Visit me!' To say David Harber makes sundials is like saying that Michaelangelo painted ceilings. David Harber makes extraordinary sundials.

The Chalice, like a cross-section of the earth with a hollow core, is a mirror-polished steel hemisphere continually overflowing with water; the hour hand (or gnomon) tells the time by casting its shadow over hand-etched hours and hour lines on the inner surface of the bowl. Then there's the Maya dial, a segmented globe comprising 24 stainless-steel semi-circles which creates the optical illusion of a solid ball at its centre. There are obelisks of semi-reflective glass illuminated from within, of stainless steel, stone or copper which act as gnomons for giant dials at ground level. The Light Sorceress is a mysterious modernistic figure gently clasping a glass time-telling disc, while the crouching statue of Atlas bears the weight of a huge armillary sphere on his back. For a spot of romance in the evening garden there's a white marble lady holding a moon dial. Then for boys who like their toys there's the Noon Day Cannon, dating from the reign of Louis XIV, which fires a shot at the appointed hour when a lens focuses the sun's rays onto a charge of gunpowder. There's even a henge of 12 monolithic stones, each one split from top to bottom to allow sunbeams to penetrate their shadows in rotation.

There are many more incredible conceits that David can conjure up for you, but I should also point out that conventional horizontal dials for mounting on plinths as well as vertical dials for walls can be tailor-made in a wide variety of styles and materials including coloured glass, slate and enamel. Whatever one you choose, each timepiece is incredibly accurate because it is engineered and calibrated for its exact latitude and longitude.

David is a great believer in sitting down over a glass of wine with clients to thrash out and evolve a design that is absolutely perfect for them. Dials can be personalized in all sorts of ways, from the engraving of birthdates and anniversaries, to aligning shafts of light with specific locations, to sealing mementoes or symbolic objects inside them. Because sundials make us aware both of our place in the cosmos and of time moving inexorably onwards, they are often inscribed with provocative mottoes. *Umbra sic vita*, for example – life is fleeting as the shadow. More intriguing still: *Quanto putas mihi strare hoc horologium?* How much do you think I paid for this sundial?

FAIRWEATHER
SCULPTURE

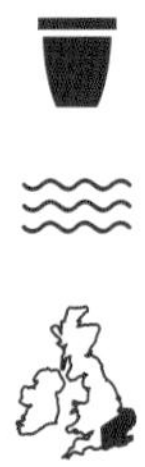

PRODUCTS INCLUDE:
Bespoke seating
Bronze resin sculptures
Ceramic sculptures
Pots & planters
Wall fountains
Water features

Fairweather Sculpture
Hillside House
Starston
Near Harleston
Norfolk
IP20 9NN
01379 852 266
www.fairweathersculpture.com
Viewing by appointment

More by accident than by design, Dennis Fairweather began developing his outdoor sculptures during the recession of the late eighties and early nineties. Art galleries were closing down everywhere, but the garden look was just beginning.

Dennis and his wife Sue took a stand at an early Hampton Court Flower Show to exhibit a hundred or so original ceramic pieces. Not only did they sell the lot, they came away with a huge number of orders. Since then, Fairweather Sculpture has been a regular annual fixture at both Chelsea and Hampton Court, with new works often featuring in display gardens.

Pieces range from life-size hares and guinea-fowl through a variety of water-features to monumental figurative and abstract works. Editions are now cast in bronze resin and carefully patinated to highlight changes in surface texture. Though Dennis's art is continually evolving, there is nevertheless a quite distinctive visual signature to his work which seduces clients into adding more and more pieces to their collections. Some people have acquired ten, twelve and even fourteen pieces.

A visit to the Museum of Cycladic Art in Athens struck a deep chord in Dennis, who was hugely inspired by the simplicity of form and enigmatic expressions of the marble figures there, which date back to more than 3,000 years BC. Their shield-like faces with long narrow noses, the tightly folded arms and the legs defined by shallow incised lines are evident in many of Dennis's human forms, be they planters or free-standing busts or figures. But this stylistic elegance also transfers to the more humorous animal pieces, with their compressed heads and bulky, distorted bodies – and in fact is what gives them the strength of character that makes them such attractive long-term additions to a garden. It can also be seen, in an even more economical form, in, say, the receptacle of a wall fountain that echoes the shape of the spouting head above, and in his massive creation Freeform with its tactile hammered outer surface and polished inner edge. This strange monolith assumes a variety of shapes according to how you approach it and reflects light differently through the course of the day. A recent development has been a commission to create a pair of seats for a Chelsea show garden based on this concept.

If you are interested in buying a piece of Fairweather sculpture but would like to see it in a garden context first, then come and visit this, Dennis and Sue's Norfolk home, where much of the work is on permanent display.

GARDEN ARCHITECTURE

Garden Architecture
259 Munster Road
Fulham
London
SW6 6BW
020 7385 1020
www.gardenarchitecture.net
Open: Mon – Fri 8 – 5
Sat 9 – 5

About the only thing I remember from economics lessons is that 'the market is where buyers and sellers meet'. Many disparate threads have to be pulled together to create a garden. Of all the businesses in this book, probably the best demonstration of the contemporary UK gardening market in action is Garden Architecture. It is a shop and gallery. It has a conservatory. It has a garden. The different areas exhibit artworks and garden products in the kind of environment they're ultimately destined for. If you see something you like, you can pick it up and take it away with you. All very tangible and straightforward. But then, if there's a piece of sculpture you like and you want to see more of the artist's work, Garden Architecture will see that you do. If you want to commission a sculptor, Garden Architecture will set the wheels in motion. If you need a lighting scheme designed and installed, then that's a company speciality, as it stocks the quality Hunza range of fittings. A one-off water feature in lead, stone or steel? Consider it done. The bespoke and the unusual are the real stock-in-trade here. In short, whatever garden dreams you might have – however adventurous, however unusual – Garden Architecture's mission is to make them a reality.

Company Manager David Haslehurst is accustomed to making things happen. He began his career as an apprentice gardener at Buckingham Palace, studied for an HND in commercial horticulture, worked in the aquatics industry, trained as a lighting consultant, and was involved for years in the landscaping of film and TV sets. Among his favourite projects were *Saving Private Ryan*, *101 Dalmatians*, *Star Wars* and the English country garden for the BBC's *Perfect Day* video. So whether you want to furnish your private sculpture garden, brighten up a courtyard with trellising, or make a stir on your Docklands rooftop with a multitude of windsocks, you should pop into Garden Architecture and get David, his team and network of contacts to sort it all out for you – without any drama.

PRODUCTS INCLUDE:
- Accent lights
- Sculpture in lead, stone and glass
- Step lights
- Trellising
- Underwater lights
- Uplighters
- Wall-mounted lights
- Water features

SCULPTORS INCLUDE:
- Shaun Brosnan
- John Brown
- Theodore Gillick
- Bernard McGuigan
- Gareth Newman
- Peter Newsome
- Carol Peace
- Antonio Lopez Reche
- Helen Sinclair
- Will Spankie
- Mike Speller
- Anthony Sturgiss

GARY DROSTLE

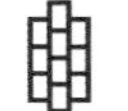

PRODUCTS INCLUDE:
Mosaics
Murals

Gary Drostle
11 Ennis Road
Plumstead
London
SE18 2QR
020 8317 2275
www.drostle.com
Works to commission

Mosaic work is one of the earliest forms of decorative art, and though its origin is uncertain, it is believed to have been first used by the Egyptians, then subsequently adopted for floor and mural decoration by the Greeks and Romans. It was extensively used by the Byzantine artists, who reintroduced it into Italy, where it continued to be practised until late in the Middle Ages. Gary Drostle is a leading contemporary exponent of mosaic, with work in private and public spaces all around the UK.

His raw materials are densely coloured vitreous ceramic and glass tesserae, and beautiful glass smalti, handmade in a centuries-old tradition by the Orsoni family of Venice. These are woven into intricate designs in Gary's Greenwich Studio prior to being laid out on site in all their glory. And because Gary always draws as much artistic inspiration as possible from that final destination, the finished mosaics are guaranteed to be fresh and exciting.

For one project, where a flight of stairs led down into a courtyard, Gary treated the risers as progressively deeper slices into the earth itself, with each tread revealing changes in soil structure and exposing archaeological finds and fossil remains. In another, a *trompe-l'oeil* fishpond suggested itself as the focal point for a quiet circular seating area. Here, great orange carp swim lazily through clear blue water, the sun casting their shadows on the base of the pool. This piece notably won an international award for Gary in 2002, and such was the acclaim that he has been asked to reprise the theme elsewhere. A particularly interesting variation was a stone horse-trough which had to be concreted over for safety reasons; Gary's mosaic not only gives back an illusion of water and of depth but makes a work of art – and a rather surreal bench – out of a sadly redundant object.

However large or small the area it covers, the real magic about mosaic is that unlike flower beds, pools or sculpture, it can bring colour, movement and visual excitement to the landscape without taking up any space. Furthermore, it requires little in the way of maintenance beyond the sweep of a broom.

Gary also creates murals in a variety of other media, but where his mosaic-work is concerned, as artist, maker and connoisseur, his eyes are passionately cast towards the ground. 'Head height is the perfect distance to view mosaics from,' he claims; 'You're just at that critical boundary of being able to take in the whole design while still being able to appreciate the detail in the work'.

If you would like to learn more about the art and craft of mosaic, Gary holds regular workshops both for beginners and for practising mosaicists who are looking to extend their skills.

GAZE-BURVILL

Gaze Burvill
Redloh House
The Old Gas Works
2 Michael Road
London
SW6 2AD
020 7471 8500
www.gazeburvill.com
Open: Mon – Fri 10 – 5.30

No tree is as much loved or held in greater esteem by the British as the oak. Standing or cut, it is probably the only tree most people today can still recognize by instinct. Quercus robur dominated the great forests that once covered much of the land and its strong, durable timber, for centuries the ultimate in building materials, is still much prized for fine-quality joinery. Besides being immensely hard wearing its distinctive, dense grain, cross-hatched with medullary rays, has a very special beauty.

With the exception of its sun loungers – which have a framework made of ash, chosen for its tough, springy resilience and lightness of weight – all of Gaze Burvill's furniture

PRODUCTS INCLUDE:
- Benches
- Chairs
- Dining tables
- Folding tables
- Love seats
- Low tables
- Planters
- Stools
- Sun loungers

is constructed in oak throughout, so comes with a great many positive associations built in even before you even consider the overall excellence of the company's designs.

The lines of all the pieces are simple and elegant, which means they suit both contemporary and traditional garden settings. There's also a stylistic coherence across all the ranges which makes it possible to mix and match them however you see fit. Best of all, there's a very tangible benefit in buying Gaze Burvill furniture. It is quite exquisitely comfortable. The reason? Rather than simply being straight slats arranged on a curve, the timbers themselves are curved to support the arch of your back and to cradle your bottom.

With consummate English craftsmanship all component pieces are sawn, steam-bent and carved into shape at the company's Hampshire workshop, and dowel joints rather than screws are used to assemble the finished pieces.

The couch seat, with its sweeping horizontal back rails has the dignity and elegance of a piece of Biedermeier, and comes as anything from a two-seater to a five-seater. A matching pair either side of a table, each echoing the other's curves, is an excellent set-up for *al-fresco* dining. If you'd like to have an outdoor sitting room too, then the Splash Collection will take your breath away: the bench is daringly designed as an expansive sofa, the seats like inviting arm chairs. There's even a coffee table.

GRAHAM GREENER

PRODUCTS INCLUDE:
Candles & flares
Cards & giftwrap
Chinese & Vietnamese pots
Cut flowers
Folding tables & chairs
Garden antiques
Lanterns
Outdoor potted plants
Terracotta plaques
Twine
Vases
Watering cans
Window boxes
Wirework

Graham Greener
27 Harbour Street
Whitstable
Kent
CT5 1AH
01227 277 100
www.grahamgreener.co.uk
Open: Mon – Sat 9 – 5.30
(Closed some Mondays in winter)
Sun 11 – 4

Famous for its hops, apples, pears and cherries, Kent has traditionally been referred to as the Garden of England. Renowned even by the Romans for the quality of its oysters, the fishing town of Whitstable has long sent the pick of its catch up to London, becoming known – you should be ahead of me here – as the Pearl of Kent. In the Middle Ages it was a convenient port of entry for continental pilgrims heading to the shrine of St Thomas à Becket in Canterbury. Today, the people going regularly to Canterbury from Whitstable are resident academics off to teach at the University of Kent. Londoners in search of peace drive down in the week to sample oysters fresh off the quayside, to buy fish in the market and to eat lunch either at the original Wheeler's or at the Whitstable Oyster Fishery Company's famous beachfront restaurant. From Friday to Monday the population grows, less with an influx of bucket-and-spade trippers than with affluent weekenders who've snapped up second homes here. What all of this means is that the quality of shopping is way in excess of what a small seaside town might be expected to offer. There's discernment, a demand for good things, and above all else, there's the money to pay for them.

There are antique shops, two excellent greengrocers, a tableware specialist, a traditional butchers, a superb chef-run delicatessen, some upmarket clothes shops, and of late there's been a fantastic flower and gardenware shop too.

Masters of ambience, Steve and Jan Graham previously ran a successful restaurant and pub design company, even hanging on to a few pubs themselves as a sideline. A few years ago they sold all of it up to enter a different phase of their lives. A spiritless insurance office was turned back into a friendly and hospitable shop with a lovely rustic feel, and the yard at the rear was gravelled over and filled with goodies. Whitstable and the Grahams became greener.

Graham Greener buys its premier-grade cut flowers direct from the Dutch auctions, imports specimen plants and shrubs from Belgian nurseries, and has a network of old business contacts all around Europe keeping back choice antique garden tools, furniture and ornaments. New items are all quality goods such as Hawes watering cans and 'green' string in jute or in seagrass. Olive and bay trees are usually potted up in imported Chinese or Vietnamese containers, and as gardening gifts the Grahams have also reprinted a series of Wills cigarette cards packed with period hints and tips. All in all, a little gem.

HANNAH PESCHAR SCULPTURE GARDEN

The Hannah Peschar Sculpture Garden
Black and White Cottage
Standon Lane
Ockley
Surrey
RH5 5QR
01306 627 269
www.hannahpescharsculpture.com
Open: Fri and Sat 11–6
Sun and Bank Hols 2–5
Tue–Thu by appointment
All the above times May–Oct
From Nov–Apr by appointment only

Art gives us pleasure in all sorts of ways, some of it simple, some of it profound. It can also cause a great deal of anxiety, especially in a stern gallery setting. What am I supposed to feel? Has it got a message? Is it all right for me to like it?

We all invest, occasionally, in expensive things but the purchasing process can make us insecure. It's silly really, but it's human nature. However, we wouldn't agonize over new sets of cutlery or crockery if we could try them out first in a restaurant rather than just looking at them in the confines of a shop. We wouldn't worry over which washing machine to install if we could give the likeliest candidates a spin at the launderette first. And computers wouldn't scare us half so witless if we could play around with them at a friend's house before buying. In precisely the same way, sculptures could be approached like old friends and new acquaintances if chanced on in a welcoming and relaxed environment. And they can be. What better place could you choose to view art for outdoors in than a garden? What better garden than this?

Nestling deep in a wooded valley, the grounds at Black and White Cottage originally formed the rock and water gardens of a much larger estate, but had sadly fallen into decay before being taken in hand and discreetly remodelled by art dealer Hannah Peschar and her landscape designer husband Anthony Paul. Reminiscent now of a tropical rainforest, the running water, dramatic massed plantings and twisting and turning pathways create the perfect backdrop for an ever-changing display of works by young and promising, mainly British, artists in materials such as wood, glass, stone, metal and fired clay.

Silvery fish swim upstream through the air, their reflections rippling beneath. Is a giant metal head still under construction, yet to find its form, or is it being ravaged by rust and decay? Light and shade give fleeting substance to wire-mesh torsos. Vibrant blue pigment transforms an elaborately carved bench. Most of the pieces are for sale, photographs of more works by the artists are on show in reception, and special commissions and studio visits can be arranged. Children are welcome, and lecture tours for parties of all ages can be booked in advance. Please note that an entrance fee is payable.

ARTISTS INCLUDE:
Paul Amey
Felicity Aylieff
Walter Bailey
David Begbie
Hannah Bennett
Maurice Blik
Graham Clayton
Alison Crowther
Fletcher and Myburgh
Bruce Gernand
Robert Harding
Rick Kirby
Andrew Schumann
Neil Wilkin
Johnny Woodford

PRODUCTS INCLUDE:
Barbecues
Candles & flares
Ceramics
Furniture
Hammocks
Garden heaters
Metal planters
Outdoor games
Parasols
Picnic hampers
Quality hand tools

Since its foundation in 1810 Heal's has had a distinctive character and a reputation for innovation. It took the aesthetic ethos of the Arts and Crafts movement very much to heart – 'have nothing in your home except what you know to be useful or believe to be beautiful' – but unlike Liberty, say, which became hidebound by the trappings of that era, Heal's has always represented the very best in contemporary design. When you cross the threshold it is impossible to believe that the company is rapidly approaching its bicentenary.

While comparing Heal's with other leading shops it is interesting to note that, like Purves and Purves nearby, it has operated since its foundation in the Tottenham Court Road, changing its premises once in 1840 due to expansion. Young urban professionals browsing the one shop will invariably browse the other, so what's the difference between the two when it actually comes to making a purchase? Well, Heal's clientele are probably a little older, have more space, are more sure of their own style and, well, they've got a bit more in the bank. More cool and collected than hip and funky.

This is apparent in the merchandising of the gardening department with a broader selection both of furniture and larger accessories, and a smaller range of what might be thought of as gift items. There are teak folding chairs and expanding tables in timeless designs, contemporary European indoor/outdoor aluminium and resin pieces, and conservatory tables, chairs and sofas that can be used outdoors on sunny days. The latter are specially imported from the Far East and are made from rattan and other natural fibres such as banana leaves and water-hyacinth fibres. There are barbecues by Weber, parasols and planters, cases of boules and massive coils of heady outdoor incense. There is also a good choice of inspirational gardening literature for sale in the adjacent book and stationery section. The flagship store carries Heal's entire outdoor collection while branches in the King's Road, in Guildford, Kingston-upon-Thames and Manchester carry a representative selection.

HORTUS

PRODUCTS INCLUDE:
- Aprons
- Barbecues
- Bird boxes
- Cards & stationery
- Children's swings
- Concrete & wood furniture
- Gloves
- Magazines
- Marble water features
- Oil burners
- Outdoor candles
- Picnic hampers
- Plants & cut flowers
- Pots & planters
- Secateurs
- Toiletries
- Tool belts
- Topiary shears
- Vases
- Weather instruments

Hortus
26 Blackheath Village
London
SE3 9SY
020 8297 9439
Open: Mon–Sat 9.30–6.00
Sun 12–5

Garden designer Joanna Herald and landscape contractor Brian Hamilton each run successful businesses of their own besides being joint proprietors of Hortus. Having been on the look-out for ages they finally found suitable premises in the middle of 2002 then spent a frantic six months sourcing products and totally refitting the store to be ready in time for Christmas. With Joanne's sense of style, Brian's technical expertise and both partners' long-established contacts in the worlds of horticulture and design, everything came together as planned. Opening trade exceeded all expectations, a regular clientele of locals has now developed, and word-of-mouth has meant that more and more people are travelling from further and further afield to browse and to buy.

The atmosphere is sleek, airy and comfortably modern. The ceiling is virtually double height, stone slabs line the floor, and a suspended canopy of timber leads boldly out through one of two plate-glass doorways into the garden at the rear. An impressive finishing touch behind the overscaled counter is the billboard-sized photograph of a lush bamboo grove. Taken by Brian on his travels in Japan, this dominates the back wall and between it and the window display you can't help but be drawn in off the street.

So what's to behold? Larger things catch the eye first, and at the time of my visit there was a faceted stainless sculpture like a tall shaft of light, a selection of sturdy but stylish concrete and wood furniture, and some enchanting children's swings like hobby-horses made from tyres and rope. There were some intriguing water features looking like columns of stacked slate but actually carved from solid pieces of black marble. There were quality folding tables and chairs in satin-finished alloy. There were tall narrow pots in polished terrazzo, and besides many other intriguing planters there were some iroko-framed window-boxes with drop-in zinc liners. These were simply begging to be filled with herbs or grasses or indeed with any of the plants outdoors specially chosen by Joanna for their looks and performance.

Smaller items on the capacious custom-built shelves included hand tools and gloves, vases and candles – objects that you'd expect of course, but of a calibre you rarely come across. The secateurs were Felco, some of the vases were in wax, the supple leather gloves had generous protective gauntlets, the barbecue lighters were in stainless steel.

Sometimes a sketch has to stand in for a full-size portrait, so to get a fuller picture I can only suggest you take a trip to Blackheath.

INDIAN OCEAN TRADING COMPANY

Indian Ocean Trading Company
155–163 Balham Hill
Clapham Common
London
SW12 9DJ
020 8675 4808
www.indian-ocean.co.uk
Open: Mon–Fri 9–6
Sat 10–6
Sun 10–4 (except Nov–Feb)

Indian Ocean specializes in outdoor teak furniture. Ten bench designs. Thirty different sizes of table. Over thirty-five chair designs. All available from stock. Enough said.

What especially interests me about the way this company works is that besides selling its wares from showrooms of its own in South London, Hampstead and Chester, it has a network of 20 or so rural partners all around the UK, some

PRODUCTS INCLUDE:
Adirondack chairs
Armchairs
Benches
Bird houses
Carvers
Decking tiles
Dining chairs
Exterior lighting
Folding chairs
Hammocks
Parasols
Patio heaters
Planters
Relaxer chairs
Stacking chairs
Sun loungers
Tables
Trays
Trolleys

of them upmarket garden centres, the bulk of them farmers looking to diversify their business. And frankly, anything that helps to keep domestic agriculture afloat earns serious brownie points in my book. Once a farm's gone, it's gone for good. Delivery is free throughout mainland UK and, besides placing an order on site, you can buy on-line, by mail-order catalogue and over the phone.

Once exposed to the elements, teak naturally weathers to a gentle silver-grey colour which sits comfortably alongside both plants and buildings, making this one of the nicest woods for outdoor furniture. It will give you years and years of wear in this condition, so don't panic when it starts to mellow. Contrary to popular belief, teak doesn't need to be oiled or, heaven forbid, varnished. Oiling can give it a mottled appearance and varnishing affects its breathability, so leave well alone. If it gets a little grubby then a quick wash and brush up with warm soapy water will soon restore its good looks.

As a testament to their quality and durability you'll find Indian Ocean's hard-wearing benches not only in private use but in public parks and gardens too. The tables, chairs and loungers do sterling work in hotels, restaurants and health clubs both here and abroad. They are also to be found in service on the seven seas aboad such luxury cruiseliners as the QEII.

To help you get as much benefit as possible from the furniture, there are some lovely accessories such as cushions, butler trays and trolleys, a lazy Susan and some walloping great patio heaters to keep you outdoors for longer. To see you through the evening, there's also a good selection of wall-mounted and bollard lights in teak, granite, rusted cast iron and a number of sleek metal finishes.

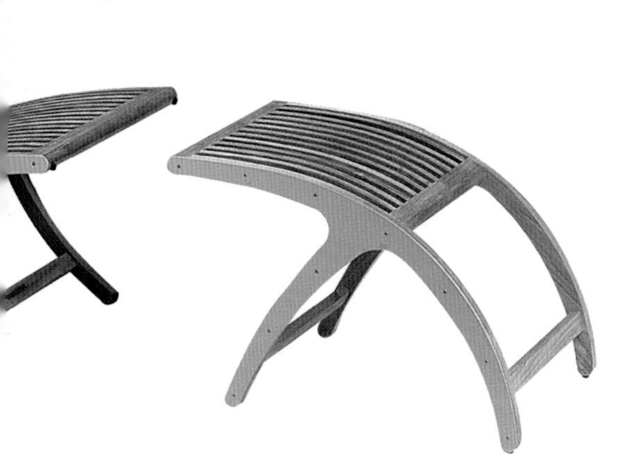

JARDINIQUE

PRODUCTS INCLUDE:
Arbours
Basketware
Bird-baths
Fountains
Gardening gifts
Gates
Hand tools
Log carriers
Ornaments
Pergolas
Plant stands
Pots & planters
Statuary
Sundials
Troughs
Urns

Jardinique
Old Park Farm
Kings Hill
Beech
Alton
Hampshire
GU34 4AW
01420 560 055
www.jardinique.co.uk
Open: Tue – Sat 10 – 5 March – Nov
Other times by appointment

Jardinique's comprehensive range of antique and contemporary garden ornament is displayed to stunning effect inside a recently converted Victorian barn, and all around a walled and railed courtyard with views across a long-established parkland landscape. It is a very fine setting indeed, and there are some incredibly grand pieces for sale, but it is a welcoming place too, and there's something here for everyone to admire and take home. Whether it's a small gift you're after, or an imposing piece of statuary, Edward and Sarah Neish pay close attention to the quality and craftsmanship of every single item they carry. For me, this kind of pre-selection is the hallmark of any good specialist retailer, be it a clothes shop or a cheesemongers. You get that lovely, reassuring feeling that somebody else has done all the hard work tracking things down for you and that you can confidently buy whatever catches your eye.

Among the new items are small bronze animals such as snails, fish, crabs and lobsters, and there are also life-size dogs and geese. There are lead cisterns and planters, greyhounds and pigs, bird-baths and classical figures. There are all kinds of basketware from flower trugs to log carriers. As well as trowels, forks and dibbers with a decent heft there are lovely leather tool-rolls, kneepads and heavy-duty suede aprons. There are cast-iron benches, cloches and urns. There are stylized wrought-iron birds as well as classically styled garden seats. There are sensibly large terracotta pots for planting things up in and splendidly daft terracotta pumpkins for planting round the garden.

Vintage pieces can include anything from sets of clock golf and croquet to boot scrapers and wheelbarrows. The selection of fine antique planters can include Coalbrookdale ironwork, Compton Pottery terracotta, and carved urns in all sorts of stone. Above all else, the statuary cannot fail to impress. The highlights of my last visit were a sleeping cherub in marble, a cast-iron gun dog, a wonderful puppy in Portland stone and a lithe Art Deco lady in lead who was actually a fountain. You, of course, will find favourites of your own to gaze on with longing.

JOHN CULLEN LIGHTING

PRODUCTS INCLUDE:
Bollard lights
Downlighters
Ground lights
Path lights
Recessed floor lights
Recessed step lights
Spotlights
Underwater spots
Uplighters

John Cullen Lighting
585 Kings Road
London
SW6 2EH
020 7371 5400
www.johncullenlighting.co.uk
Open: Mon – Fri 9.30 – 5.30
Sat 10 – 4
(except Bank Holiday weekends)

Say the word 'lighting' to an amateur gardener and to a designer, and you'll conjure up entirely different images in their minds. Garden lighting from the high street or the DIY hangar is usually to do with the lamp itself as a decorative object. Professional work is about the creation of special effects with light pure and simple – its magic lies in concealing, so far as possible, the source of that light.

The fittings at John Cullen are chosen for their creative lighting potential, discreet appearance, performance and good design. While some come in an olive-green finish, others are made of copper which ages to verdigris. The end result is the same: they disappear amongst your plants. Some are fitted flush into walls and groundworks, others come on spikes to allow for easy repositioning as your garden matures.

Good lighting maximizes the use of your garden and increases your enjoyment of it. Seen from indoors, a well-lit garden draws the eye, visually extending the house to give a greater feeling of space. When the weather is warm, and you're outdoors at nightfall, the garden can become a place of wonder. A dramatically uplit tree creates one mood; the same tree with moonlight apparently filtering down through its branches evokes quite another response. Where an old brick wall might be gently grazed with light to enhance its texture, a modern concrete or rendered surface might be charged with colour in a bold architectural statement. Pools of dappled light might lead the way through dense primeval foliage or crisp and striking shadows of grass or bamboo might be cast around a courtyard.

To demonstrate the different options available, the John Cullen showroom has full blackout facilities, enabling you to experience a range of effects at first hand. This might be all that is needed to help you decide on which fittings to install. Alternatively, if you've got a good set of plans then by prior appointment you can book a thorough consultation. The best thing of all, though, is to arrange for a designer to visit your home and draw up a tailor-made lighting scheme. It's quite an investment, of course, but the return is phenomenal. Close your eyes, visualize your garden, then think of 'lighting' again. Oh, the possibilities...

JUDY GREENE'S GARDEN STORE

PRODUCTS INCLUDE:
Antique items
Barbecues
Baskets
Carriers
Garden heaters
Gloves
Fine hand tools
Pots & planters
Potted plants

Judy Greene's Garden Store
11 Flask Walk
Hampstead
London
NW3 1HJ
020 7435 3832
Open: Mon–Sat 10–6
Sun 12–6

Down around the corner from Hampstead tube station, then round the corner again, and you'll find the small but perfectly formed Flask Walk, a rather smart pedestrian alleyway discreetly lined with shops and galleries. A few doors along on the left, perfectly in character with its surroundings, and with a beautiful pavement display outside, you're irresistibly drawn to the Garden Store begun in 1996 by Judy Greene, wife of Colefax and Fowler's David Greene.

After completing an intensive one-year course at the English Gardening School, based at the Chelsea Physic Garden, Judy embarked on a career in garden design – but with her gregarious, outgoing personality she found it, to be honest, a rather lonely pursuit. Then almost out of nowhere, the idea of a gardening shop came into her head. 'It's always hard when you get excited about something to know what actually sets you off, but I'd just been in the States and came across the retail and publishing chain Smith and Hawken. And I've always loved places like The Conran Shop and Habitat where you can buy things from £5 to £500 but where everything is very, very lovely. And of course, plants are always at the forefront of my mind.' Now, I have to declare a personal interest here, because a very dear friend's parents used to live across the High Street from Judy's shop, and it was always a perfect source of last-minute cards and presents on the way to dinner: little pots of scented narcissi wrapped beautifully in tissue paper and twine, orchids in abundance, fragrant herbs and scented candles, ferns and camellias, cyclamen and lilies.

More substantial items include baskets and carriers; contemporary and antique gardening equipment including some fantastic turn-of-the-century watering cans; standard lavender bushes and olive trees potted up ready for siting. If you really want to push the boat out there are startlingly original concrete planters by Christine Wild and one-off pieces created by artist potter Jane Norbury in a sleepy village just outside Mâcon in France. Norbury incises abstract patterns in the wet clay or embosses it with leaves before giving the resulting forms a gentle, chalky wash to enhance their subtle texture and relief.

One of the Garden Store's most enduring successes has been its famous Burmese terracotta barbecue. When it was first introduced, a review in a national paper set the phone ringing off the hook, and demand was so great Judy had to return early from holiday to assist her staff. Well done!

JULIAN CHICHESTER
Julian Chichester
Studio S
The Old Imperial Laundry
71 Warriner Gardens
London
SW11 4XW
020 7274 8899
www.julianchichester.com
Open: Mon – Fri 9.30 – 6

PRODUCTS INCLUDE:
Armchairs
Benches
Carvers
Children's chairs
Dining chairs
Folding chairs
Parasols
Planters
Sun loungers
Tables

An amazing centre for designers, decorators, dealers in art and antiques and all kinds of esoteric craft workers, this converted laundry near Battersea Park is positively bursting at the seams with talent. It is the kind of place where half the clientele is made up of architects and interior designers sourcing or specifying products for their clients, and the other half consists of serious shoppers bent on fulfilling all their dreams themselves.

Though perhaps best known in the wider world for his luxurious home furnishings, which include both original designs and contemporary interpretations of classic pieces from the Regency period up to the 1950s, Julian Chichester is thought of first and foremost by gardeners in the know as a maker of distinctive outdoor tables and chairs.

In fact, the outdoor collection came first but drew its inspiration in part from the designs of master cabinet-makers. The intricate fretwork of the Wicklow bench mirrors the fine lines of a Chippendale library desk; the crossing lines and elliptical curves in the back-rest of the Beaulieu might resemble the scrolls on a banknote but they are derived from a Hepplewhite bookcase; the exquisitely simple lozenge-and-cross pattern on the Exbury comes from a piece by Sheraton. Other of his ranges reflect the twentieth-century call for simpler and straighter

lines, but all share the timeless appeal that only good design can bestow.

An interesting recent addition is the Chiltern bench created by Franziska von Groll, winner of a student design competition sponsored by the company. Asymmetric in form and composed of a rolling sweep of parallel laths, it is incredibly clean lined yet has a complex dynamism, making it an object of real beauty that deserves a position where it can be admired from as many different angles as possible.

Teak is the timber that is used throughout; contemporary pieces incorporate structural elements in powder-coated steel and some of the tabletops are solid sheets of slate.

KATHY DALWOOD

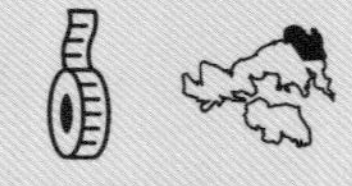

PRODUCTS INCLUDE:
Planters
Tiles
Vases

Kathy Dalwood
165 Victoria Road
London
NW6 6TE
020 7372 2677
www.kathydalwood.fsnet.co.uk
Viewing by appointment

Concrete acquired a reputation as a brutal medium largely through its widespread use as a cheap building material both in post-war public housing schemes and also in the redevelopment of city centres in the sixties and seventies. In neither case can the architects and designers be called to account: times were hard, the population was soaring, and utility on a budget was the order of the day. Never mind the imaginative use made of concrete by the Modernist movement, council estates of le Corbusier villas were quite out of the question.

Concrete today is undergoing a renaissance. Aside from the fleeting cachet of retro chic, it is reaching new heights in luxurious apartment developments and office complexes where comfort and aesthetics are of prime consideration. Sheer planes and sweeping curves of concrete can be enormously seductive: courtyards can merge seamlessly with walls, walls with balconies and roof terraces, the outside with the inside.

With homes making use of glass, steel and unadorned wood, concrete is in fact an entirely sympathetic material. In a modern urban context, traditional stone or terracotta planters can look out of place at best, affected at worst. This is where the work of people like Kathy Dalwood with her cast collection comes into its own.

The fact that concrete is poured and only acquires form when it is cast and set creates interesting opportunities for decorative relief. Kathy's forms and abstract surface patterns derive from architectural, industrial and engineering details, so suit the medium perfectly, giving her pieces both an internal logic and forging a stylistic bond with their surroundings. Grain silos, gateposts, the profiles of roofs, the intersections of walls by doors and windows all play a part in her work. Some pieces play with the use of exposed aggregate; others are smoothly finished but highly coloured. Some will hold a single small succulent; others, almost a metre in length, offer dramatic planting opportunities.

A recent logical development has been a move into unglazed cast ceramic tiles, which work as textural installations in both interior and exterior locations. Both the tiles and the planters are manufactured in the UK, and because of the handmade element in the production process, even small orders can be customized in terms of colour while series can be commissioned to any scale.

KING DOVECOTES

PRODUCTS INCLUDE:
Bat boxes
Bird boxes
Bird feeders
Bird tables
Chicken houses
Chicken runs
Dovecotes
Feed pots
Homing boxes

King Dovecotes
75 Copthorne Road
Felbridge
East Grinstead
Sussex
RH19 2PB
01342 324 159
www.kingdovecotes.co.uk
Open: Please telephone ahead

Doves are found in one form or another in almost every part of the world, and they have a long association with mankind, but one which was not always so romantic as you might imagine. Dovecotes have been built since the time of the Pharaohs, but up until a couple of hundred years ago in the UK, ownership was the exclusive preserve of noblemen and wealthy landowners, and their purpose was strictly utilitarian: to provide a ready supply of food, both meat and eggs, for the table. No more regard was given to their aesthetic appeal than to cowsheds or pigsties, and some could hold up to 3,000 pairs of doves.

All this changed in the Victorian era when fluttering snow-white doves, symbols of peace, freedom and innocence in Christian art, captured the popular imagination and gave designers food for thought. Daintily beautiful dovecotes were created and sited in full view of the home where both they and their billing and cooing inhabitants could be admired as purely decorative garden elements.

Today, that Victorian tradition is kept alive by David King and his family, whose hand-crafted pine dovecotes come in a range of styles and sizes to suit all tastes and pockets. His ten-sided top-of-the-range King's Folly has five holes on each of its storeys so is capable of holding up to 20 pairs of doves. It soars over 5m (16ft) into the air on a massive pressure-treated post, and a fully tiled roof crowned with a copper top and finial keeps the whole thing snug and dry. The Barn House, at the other end of the property ladder provides attractive back-to-back accommodation for just two nest-making young couples. Doves – it should be pointed out – mostly mate for life, so David only sells his exquisite White Fantails in pairs.

Other free-standing models include the octagonal Tudor, housing 12 pairs like the beamed Elizabethan; the black and white Millhouse with its steeply pitched roof, the pagoda-like brilliant red Oriental and the elegant white Classic, all holding eight pairs. For the smaller garden, the single storey Windsor provides sovereign accommodation for four pairs. If ground space is at a premium, consider the Victorian wall cote, which comes in a variety of sizes, or plump for the six-pair Edwardian.

Any of the standard designs can be painted and finished to your own specifications and bespoke orders are always welcome. Indeed, one not uncommon sight is 'mini-me' reproductions of clients' own homes.

THE KITCHEN GARDEN

PRODUCTS INCLUDE:
Bird houses
China eggs
Cloches
Corn scoops
Dovecotes
Drinkers
Feeders
Gloves
Hen-houses
Honey
Labels
Plants & seedlings
Seed boxes
Tools

The Kitchen Garden
Church Lane
Troston
Bury St Edmunds
Suffolk
IP31 1EX
01359 268 322
www.kitchen-garden-hens.co.uk
Open: Fri – Sat 10 – 6
May – July and Sep – Oct
(Please telephone ahead)

As you might have deduced from its eccentric business hours, The Kitchen Garden is no ordinary shop but a rather civilized and quintessentially English enterprise. Just across the road from a village church in deepest Suffolk, Francine Raymond opens the doors of her cottage from Easter to Harvest (closed in August) to serve such treats as strawberry teas and freshly baked elderflower and sweet Cicely sponge. As a keen gardener she sells locally raised plants and vegetable seedlings along with seedboxes, labels and gloves, complemented by a carefully selected range of tools. As a connoisseur of the good life, she sells homemade seasonal produce including honey fresh from the comb. Most important of all, as a hen-keeper of many years standing she dabbles in poultry paraphernalia from her own backyard.

There's a galvanized corn scoop with a wooden handle for scattering feed and for collecting eggs. There are cloches woven from split bamboo to keep tender young salad leaves in the peak of perfection until you want to peck at them. There are even china eggs for spurring broody hens into action and for suggesting that chucks with a wanderlust lay a little closer to home. Don't laugh, they work. Hens are simple souls. Last but not least, there are hen-houses and dovecotes. And when teatime comes around, there are hand-thrown blue-and-white checked egg cups with matching spoons. Thoughtfully, Francine sells two sizes: regular hen and titchy bantam.

An author and publisher too, Francine has produced a series of books including *Keeping a Few Hens in Your Garden*, *Keeping a Few Ducks in Your Garden* and *Beekeeping for Beginners*, all of which can be ordered by post or bought on the spot. If you're planning to make a special trip to Troston, then do phone in advance to check that Francine will be around as well as to find out if there are any special events on the horizon: there's usually a Hen Party on Easter Sunday, a Honey Fair on the first Saturday in September, and there are ten Christmas shopping days at the beginning of December. There are occasional hen-rearing workshops too, and lessons on egg cookery.

According to the Talmud 'if a man sees a cockerel in a dream, he may expect a son; if several cocks, several sons; if a hen, a fine garden and rejoicing'. There's much rejoicing in The Kitchen Garden.

LASSCO

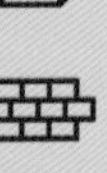

PRODUCTS INCLUDE:
Archways
Balcony fronts
Columns
Finials
Fossils
Fountains
Gates
Gazebos
Lampposts
Pedestals & plinths
Plant stands
Pulpits
Railings
Seating
Statuary
Stonework
Sundials
Weathervanes
Windows

LASSCO
St Michael's Church
Mark Street (off Paul Street)
London
EC2A 4ER
020 7749 9944
www.lassco.co.uk
Open: Mon – Sat 10 – 5

LASSCO Flooring (020 7394 2101), RBK (020 7394 2102) and Warehouse (020 7394 2103) are at 41 Maltby Street, London SE1 3PA.

More of an empire than a mere company, the London Architectural Salvage and Supply Co. has five divisions trading from two distinct sites, so you need to be sure where you're heading. LASSCO Warehouse (architectural salvage), LASSCO Flooring (pretty self-explanatory) and LASSCO RBK (that's radiators, bathrooms and kitchens) are all in Bermondsey. LASSCO St Michael's (architectural antiques) and LASSCO Home and Garden are both housed rather spectacularly in a stunning Victorian church in Shoreditch.

Now, my sense of direction, which is shaky at the best of times, goes absolutely to pot when it comes to finding St Michael's – and I've been going there at least twice a year for the best part of a decade. Don't set off without an A–Z. Though it's actually within spitting distance of the intersection of Old Street and City Road, LASSCO seems regularly to disappear into some strange Bermuda Triangle all of its very own. Either that, or it teeters on the edge of a break in the space/time continuum. Laugh if you will, but you have been warned.

Any frustration you might experience getting there dissipates the moment you enter. As you walk in through the porch – especially for the first time – you're filled with a sense of wonder and amazement. The church itself is packed to the rafters with all sorts of unimaginable treasures; the yard at the back is stuffed to bursting point. It is as though the place is run by a lunatic vicar in league with the Victoria & Albert Museum.

Coming from such prestigious places as West End banks, City office buildings, churches and aristocratic homes, the larger pieces – marble columns, balcony fronts, stained-glass windows, carriage gates, stone archways and pulpits – are really the province of architects and property developers. It's the ultimate in recycling really. Smaller items of salvage though, and the free-standing garden antiques, will tempt you beyond belief. Besides selling original statuary in lead, stone and bronze, LASSCO has some great reproductions in stock too and there are also editions that have been specially commissioned by the company from living artists. Don't be afraid just to stand and stare, you can always salve your conscience on the way out by stocking up on lovely old terracotta flowerpots at a pound or so a throw. That's what I do. If gorgeous things for the garden are your holy grail, you'll think you've died and gone to heaven at St Michael's.

LEISUREPLAN

PRODUCTS INCLUDE:
Armchairs
Bar stools
Benches
Bistro tables
Coffee tables
Day beds
Dining chairs
Dining tables
Directors chairs
Foot stools
Side chairs
Side tables
Sofas
Sun loungers
Trolleys

MANUFACTURERS INCLUDE:
Dedon
Fischer Mobel
Hugonet
Triconfort

Leisure Plan
Silver Street
Stansted Mountfitchet
Essex
CM24 8HD
01279 816 001
www.leisureplan.co.uk
Open: Mon – Fri 10 – 4

Managing Director Chris McCormack set up his company with the express intention of bringing the very best in European outdoor furniture to the UK. The ranges he has introduced are exclusive to Leisure Plan and have an éclat and sophistication that instantly marks them out as in a league quite of their own.

When you look at the gleaming white lacquered resin ware from Triconfort you think immediately of Riviera poolsides. The sofas, armchairs and sun loungers can be fitted with luxurious, mattress-like cushions; there are canopies to keep the glare off your face; and substantial back wheels make them easy to manoeuvre.

The teak pieces can be kitted out with upholstery too, but that's hardly necessary as they are all distinguished by slatted seats and back rests curved to the contours of the human form. Among the interesting tables – round and square, folding and extending – is a nifty little side or 'balcony' table adjustable to three different heights.

The aluminium furniture is something else too, conjuring up enticing images of private yachts in azure blue marinas. The tubular frames come in a wide range of lacquers, and you can also choose the colour of the taut vinyl polyester meshes that make the seats and loungers so unforgettably comfortable.

The most extraordinary garden furniture you'll ever come across though is the Dedon range. Handwoven in the Philippines, it looks fantastic in any setting but really comes into its own against lush tropical plantings.

You could be forgiven for thinking these exotic pieces, which come in white, seagrass, natural, java (a rich coffee colour) and bronze were for conservatory use only. But you'd be wrong. Entirely natural in appearance, they are made out of a synthetic material called Hularo once used in the ski industry. Never mind a spot of rain, they are impervious to snow and ice. There are several different collections, stylistically evoking the places they are named for: Panama, the Hamptons, Havana, Key West, the Orient. Sit back, and dream on...

MARSTON & LANGINGER

Marston & Langinger
192 Ebury Street
London
SW1W 8UP
020 7881 5717
www.marston-and-langinger.com
Open: Mon – Fri 10 – 6
Sat 10 – 5

Marston and Langinger Factory Shop
George Edwards Road
Fakenham
Norfolk
NR21 8NL
01328 852 540
Open: Mon – Fri 10 – 5
from Easter until end Sept Sat 10 – 4

In the early seventeenth century, Dutch horticulturalists began using glass screens to conserve tender plants through the cold winter months. By the eighteenth century their simple structures had evolved to become the grand classical orangeries of the European nobility, and by the early nineteenth century the widespread use of cast iron saw the flourishing of the great glasshouses, such as Decimus Burton's Palm House at Kew and Joseph Paxton's Crystal Palace for the Great Exhibition.

On a domestic scale, conservatories came into their own in Victorian Britain when they were filled with exotic plants from around the empire. A symbol of affluence to this day, the modern conservatory is a welcome addition to any home just as long as it blends seamlessly with house and garden.

Peter Marston, a graduate of St Martin's College of Art, combined his architectural knowledge with his love of gardening by founding, in 1972,

PRODUCTS INCLUDE:

Cabinet work
Cedar blinds
Conservatories
Fabric blinds
Fabrics
Glassware
Greenhouses
Hand tools
Heating
Lighting
Metal chairs & tables
Paints
Pinoleum blinds
Pots & baskets
Staging
Watering cans
Willow furniture
Wirework

a company that now designs and builds conservatories, orangeries, pool houses and garden rooms all around the world and which offers all the flooring, furniture, fixtures and fittings you could ever need to kit them out in style.

Each project is designed to reflect the spirit of its surrounding architecture, so the conservatory for a Regency brick-and-flint villa will look as though it were always part of the house, a clapboard-based greenhouse will be a sympathetic addition to the garden and an extension to a shady basement flat will bring much-needed light to the interior.

Flooring materials include handmade English terracotta, Tuscan limestone flecked with fossils and traditional Cotswold flags. Doors, windows and garden woodwork can be made to match any style and period – past customers include English Heritage and the National Trust. Temperature and ventilation systems are available to respect the needs of plants and people alike.

Just a stone's throw from Sloane Square, the London shop and design studio is packed to the skylights with rugs, chairs, tables, tools, framed prints, lamps, pots and crockery. There's even an exclusive paint collection with a range of sophisticated off-whites and such tempting colours as Etruscan Red, Delft and Pistachio.

All the frameworks are built at the company's Norfolk workshops prior to being assembled and glazed on site. Drop in if you're passing, because there's a discount factory shop selling slightly imperfect stock, ex-display goods from exhibitions such as the Chelsea Flower Show, ends of ranges and prototypes.

THE MODERN GARDEN COMPANY

The Modern Garden Company
Millars 3
South Mill Road
Bishops Stortford
Hertfordshire
CM23 3DH
01279 653 200
www.moderngarden.co.uk
Telephone enquiries Mon – Fri 9 – 5
Showroom viewing by appointment

Spotting a gap in the retail market for good quality design-led outdoor furniture, Caroline Calvert and Lynne Isham founded The Modern Garden Company at the very end of 1999. Smart thinking. From the dawn of the new millennium they have been leading players in the field, not only selling direct to discerning members of the general public and the rock, pop and footballing fraternities but to professional garden designers and commercial organisations like bars, restaurants and health clubs. They have furnished numerous gardens at both the Chelsea and Hampton Court flower shows, and not a few of their products have made guest appearances on television make-over programmes.

A classic of twentieth-century design, Willy Guhl's 1954 Loop chair is hand moulded in reinforced concrete and mellows beautifully with age. Conceived 45 years later, yet visually of a piece, the sinuous Loop table can be stored inside the chair when not in use.

Effortlessly supporting oiled teak slats in pearl-blasted stainless steel frames, the Natal range by Wim Segers looks as good in a traditional as in a contemporary setting and includes chairs, tables, a trolley and a hypnotically clean-lined sun lounger you can't help but covet.

Whether you look at Verner Panton's amoebic polypropylene Phantom – which can be a one- or two-seater chair, a table or a lounger according to how you orientate it – or Stemmer & Sharp's subtly styled and seriously expensive Straight Forward lounger or Jasper Morrison's easily affordable, candy-coloured Air-Chairs, I guarantee that the Modern Garden Company's stock will open up whole new horizons on maximizing the potential of your outdoor space.

Caroline and Lynne have a website and a mail-order catalogue in addition to their showroom, and they are also delighted to discuss individual requirements by phone. Many items are available from stock, while other pieces are made to order, so your imagination and their expertise can produce some original, truly stunning combinations. When the Eden Project wanted to commission hard-wearing benches made entirely of recycled materials, the Modern Garden Company was a natural choice.

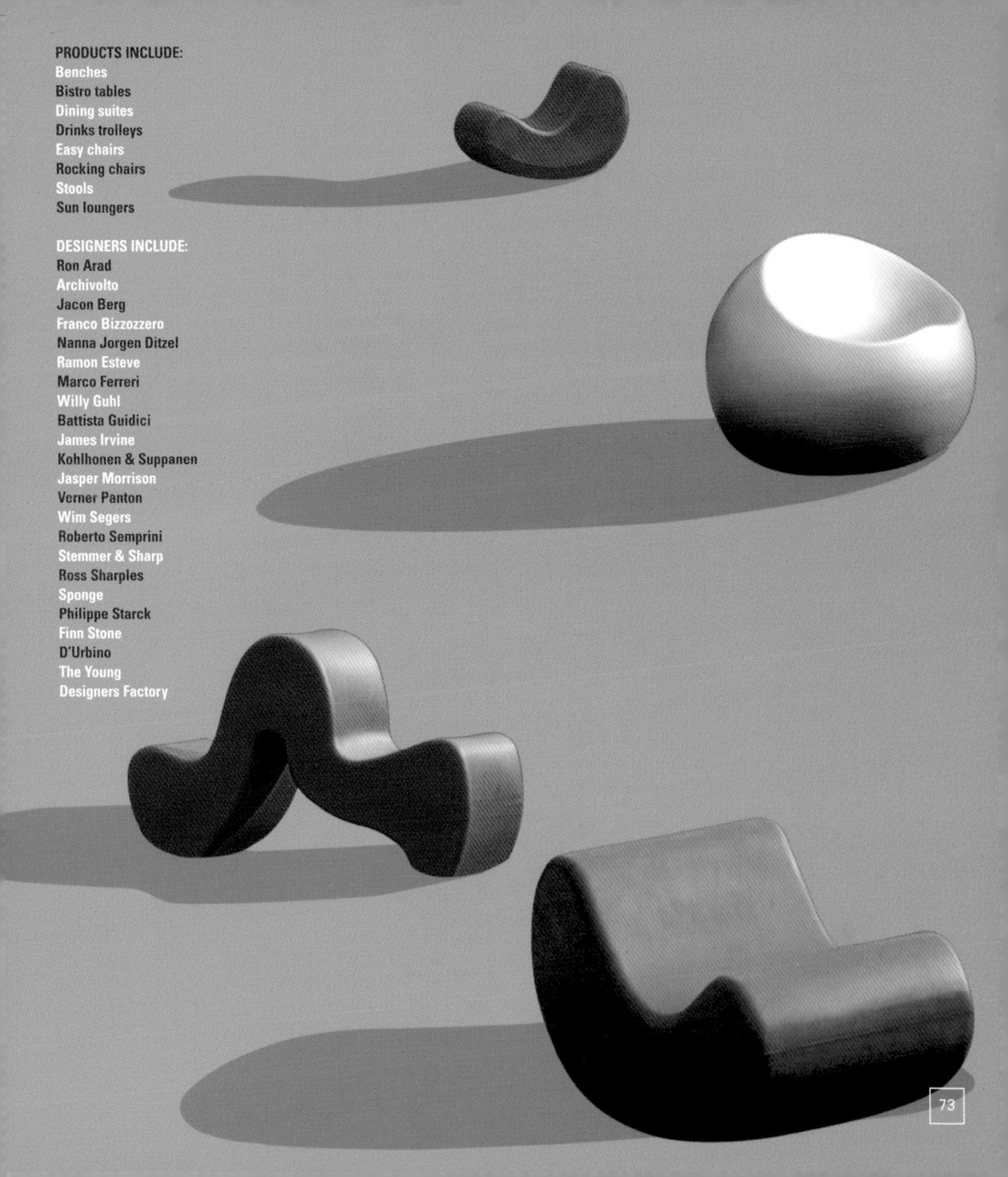

PRODUCTS INCLUDE:
Benches
Bistro tables
Dining suites
Drinks trolleys
Easy chairs
Rocking chairs
Stools
Sun loungers

DESIGNERS INCLUDE:
Ron Arad
Archivolto
Jacon Berg
Franco Bizzozzero
Nanna Jorgen Ditzel
Ramon Esteve
Marco Ferreri
Willy Guhl
Battista Guidici
James Irvine
Kohlhonen & Suppanen
Jasper Morrison
Verner Panton
Wim Segers
Roberto Semprini
Stemmer & Sharp
Ross Sharples
Sponge
Philippe Starck
Finn Stone
D'Urbino
The Young
Designers Factory

OTTER
WROUGHT IRON

WEATHERVANE DESIGNS INCLUDE:
Aircraft
Animals
Birds
Boats
Breeds of dog
Cars
Cats
Horses
Livestock
Motorbikes
Music & dance
Mythical figures
Sport & recreation themes
Tractors & working vehicles
Trains, lorries & buses

OTHER PRODUCTS INCLUDE:
Hanging baskets
House name signs
House number signs
Plant stands
Wall planters
Wall plaques

Otter Wrought Iron
12 Fourth Avenue
Bluebridge
Halstead
Essex
CO9 2SY
01787 475 060
www.weathervanes.co.uk
Workshop visits by appointment

Simple devices whose mechanisms hold no secrets are deeply fascinating. In our technological age their mystery is that mystery is stripped bare. Thermos flasks keep hot drinks hot and cold drinks cold yet they require neither power nor instruction. Ballcocks safely and tirelessly refill cisterns just by floating up on the water they deliver. The hypnotic swaying arcs of lawn sprinklers are merely mains pressure made manifest. The shadows on sundials mark the movements of the heavens. They allow us to see the invisible, helping us to contemplate the world's natural forces.

As the New Testament says 'The wind bloweth where it listeth, and thou hearest the sound thereof, but canst not tell whence it cometh, and whither it goeth.' Unless, that is, thou hast a weathervane. What simpler or more satisfying object could you buy to admire outdoors?

Norman and Gillian Massey sell their weathervanes all around the country at gardening and agricultural shows, by mail order and from their workshop – if you can catch them there between events. There are three sizes to choose from: petite, for sheds, conservatories and small outbuildings; medium, for garages, stables and bungalows; large, for houses and barns. They are made in best-quality British steel, come in two grades (the deluxe is advised for coastal locations), and can be mounted on posts, gable ends or the ridge of the roof. Your choice of one of five fixing brackets is included in the cost so installation is perfectly straightforward. Just make sure that whoever does the work has a compass handy for aligning the cardinal points. And in case you've any nagging doubt, the silhouette 'sail' goes with the flow, so the arrow points into the wind, towards its source. Many a time Norman and Gillian have been asked to settle bets on the subject.

The Masseys are rightly proud of their silhouette designs. Some, of course, are traditional but the majority are original creations, and they now offer a choice fast approaching five hundred. Crisply cut by laser, the detail can be staggering. Elements from different vanes can be combined for a one-off piece, or you can commission something that's quite unique. Gold leaf can be applied to contrast with the black, and local artists are on hand to paint them in colour if you wish. Basically, the sky's the limit.

POTS AND PITHOI

PRODUCTS INCLUDE:
Antique pottery
Beehive pots
Blue glazed earthenware
Citrus pots
Hand-blown glass
Oil jars
Shallow planters
Tubs
Urns
Water features

Pots and Pithoi
The Barns
East Street
Turners Hill
West Sussex
RH10 4QQ
01342 714 793
www.potsandpithoi.com
Open: Mon – Sun 10 – 5
(4 in winter)
Closed: December 24 – January 2
and all weekends in January

As soon as you pull into Pots and Pithoi's car park off the B2110 and stroll across the gravel you sense that something rather magical awaits. This is more like a garden visit than a shopping trip. Rosie and Robin Lloyd house their vast stock of Cretan terracotta inside and all around a large courtyard of beautifully converted cattle barns. Lots of the containers are imaginatively planted up to give you plenty of inspiration, and gentle and unobtrusive staff are always on hand with advice and information.

There are more than 14,000 garden, patio and conservatory pots for sale in 96 styles and 240 sizes. No two will be exactly alike as they are all individually thrown by craftsmen potters using traditional methods dating back over 3,000 years. Ranging in colour from mellow yellow through subtle biscuit tones to stone-like greige, they have an immediate affinity with earth, foliage and flowers that those mass-produced wares in angry orange dream long and hard for. Take plenty of time to mull over your choices and your instincts will guide you ineluctably towards those pieces that will merge perfectly into your home and garden landscape.

The smaller, competitively priced, pots look gorgeous in informal groups, whether filled afresh each year with bulbs and annuals or used as permanent showcases for treasured perennials. The larger urns make striking focal points, especially when planted with trees or hardy palms; they can also be left empty, all the better to appreciate their strong sculptural presence. A third option is to have the pot of your choice converted into a water feature – the horizontally ribbed Beehive pots look and sound fantastic as they burble and overflow either into a shallow circular pool or onto a child-friendly base of pebbles. (Don't worry about your back, nationwide and worldwide delivery can be arranged.)

Standing in silent testimony to the durability of its modern-day merchandise, Pots and Pithoi has amassed a notably fine collection of beautifully patinated antique pots from Turkey, Greece, Portugal and Spain. For the price of a family car, high earners can splash out on towering great oil jars more than 1,000 years old, but you'll be relieved to know that smaller pieces of history fall within everyone's grasp.

As if all this weren't enough, the shop sells an array of Mediterranean housewares and certain foods including olive oil and honey. What's more, you never know what bargains are to be found among the flawed and damaged pots round the back. Beware. A one-off look-see could be the start of a habit.

PURVES & PURVES

Purves & Purves
220 – 4 Tottenham Court Road
London
W1T 7QE
020 7580 8223
www.purves.co.uk
Open: Mon – Sat 9.30 – 6
except Tue 10 – 6 and Thu 9.30 – 7.30
Sun 11.30 – 5.30

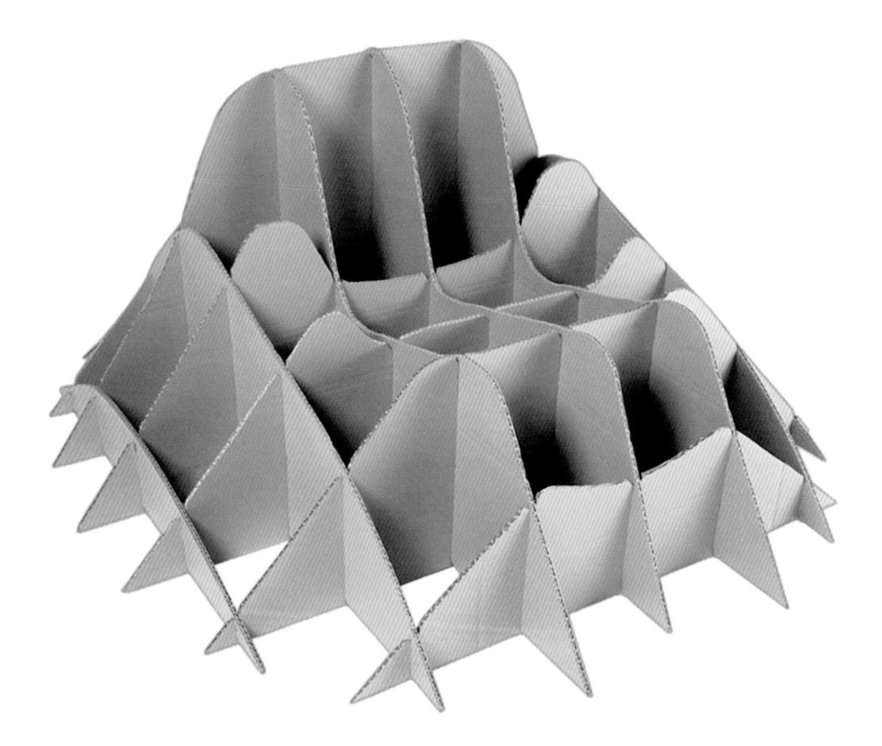

PRODUCTS INCLUDE:
Chrome lanterns
Contemporary seating
Garden flares
Grass seats
Herb-growing kits
Metal planters
Patio heaters
'Pebble' planters
Watering cans
Weather instruments

To fill superstore-sized premises with boutique-quality goods is no mean achievement. Already operating from a sizeable space across the road when it opened in 1992, the move to its present site in 2001 not only marked Purves & Purves as one of the UK's most exciting and accessible lifestyle retailers, it also demonstrated that good, challenging design really can be a commercially viable high-street commodity.

Selling furniture and lighting, kitchenware and accessories, boys' toys and girlie goodies, Purves & Purves can furnish the contemporary home from top to bottom – and in the case of lateral conversions, from side to side. With the modern trend in architecture and interior decoration increasingly making greater connections between indoor and outdoor spaces, it is only natural that the ever-changing product range should therefore include a wide range of garden-related products – both high-end furnishings and gift-priced gadgets.

MD Andrew Purves notes an increasing cross-over between indoor and outdoor items, evidenced in store by Philippe Starck's smoothly rounded Zbork chair and Ploof sofa in futuristic plastics which work on a balcony or roof-terrace or in the sitting room. Stainless-steel watering cans manufactured with surgical precision not only fulfil their function by pouring beautifully, they are the kind of thing you'd happily display indoors, rather than consigning them to a shed or cupboard – assuming you even have such things. The modern living space is all too often a small one: storage is out while versatility and good looks are in.

For me, the most thought-provoking products consist of flat-pack recycled cardboard kits which slot together to form either an armchair or a sofa. These are sited on your lawn, filled with earth, then planted up with the grass seed provided. Once growth is established you've got an incredibly stable, surprisingly comfortable and very attractive seat. Post-modern ironic or just plain old common-sense? You decide.

In a consumer society retailers, by default, become the new galleries, but Purves & Purves has the vision actively to promote dialogue between young designers and potential customers by hosting exhibitions of new and upcoming work. One such was their 'Pining for It' show which commissioned work striving to create a new paradigm for the use of softwood in furniture, an outstanding piece being a barrel-shaped outdoor bench by Chris Lefteri. Unlike many galleries though, Purves & Purves has low-key staff and a welcoming atmosphere. Feel free to look, linger, have lunch or a coffee – you'll always leave the shop refreshed and stimulated.

R K ALLISTON

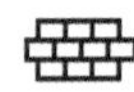

R K Alliston
173 New Kings Road
London
SW6 4SW
Open: Mon – Fri 9 – 6
Sat 10 – 6

6 Quiet Street
Bath
Somerset
BA1 2JS
Open: Mon – Sat 9.30 – 6
Sun 11 – 5

0845 130 5577
www.rkalliston.com

Smartly painted black with two large and beautifully arranged display windows, the imposing corner-site HQ in London's Parsons Green would make any passer-by stop and take note even if it weren't for the enormous gnarled olive tree in a huge pot outside the front door. The soil that the tree grows in is topped off with a decorative layer of crushed scallop shells, aptly indicative of owner Harriet Scott's impeccable eye for detail. It also shows a keen business brain: miniature olive trees and sacks of scallop-shell mulch in either pink or grey are available within.

Harriet grew up in a Surrey garden created by Gertrude Jekyll, studied at the Inchbald School of Design, then spent three years on the staff of two very different landscape companies, one traditional, one avant-garde, before branching out on her own in 1996. R K Alliston, named for her artist grandfather who gardened in the south of France, is the fruit of these labours. It stocks an extensive range of stylish products for garden lovers in both its London and Bath shops, offers mail-order through a catalogue and a website, and provides a comprehensive service to design, build and maintain any and every kind of outdoor space.

As you would expect from someone with both the English Home Counties and the Mediterranean as sources of inspiration, with a sense of history and a finger on the pulse of the contemporary gardening scene, Harriet has an eclectic range of products, but craftsmanship, beauty and practicality unify them all to create a distinctive R K Alliston 'look'. There are hand-thrown terracotta thumb-pot waterers as found in medieval engravings. There are French bypass secateurs and flower cutters with leather-trimmed handles for a comfortable grip. Besides the Le Chameau range of wellingtons and gardening boots there's some stylish Italian workwear and a rather nifty gardening apron for children. To decorate the garden and conservatory there are slate herb boxes, pot holders and glass bauble lights and for recreation there are croquet sets and boules. To soothe aching limbs at the end of the day there's the exclusive le plaisir du jardinier range of scrubs, creams and oils with such gorgeous fragrances as lemon and myrrh, bergamot and geranium or lavender and teatree. What bliss!

PRODUCTS INCLUDE:
Bird houses
Candles
Clothing
Dibbers
Footwear
Games
Garden journals
Kneelers
Lamps
Planters
Pruning knives
Secateurs
Shears
Toiletries
Trugs

RAYMENT WIREWORK

PRODUCTS INCLUDE:

- Arbour seats
- Archways
- Aviaries
- Candelabra
- Canopy seats
- Chandeliers
- Conversation seats
- Hanging baskets
- Hanging chairs
- Jardinières
- Obelisks
- Pavilions
- Rose arbours
- Rose walks
- Stools
- Tables
- Topiary frames
- Trellises
- Urns
- Window boxes

Rayment Wirework
Unit 7
Hoo Farm
Monkton Road
Minster-in-Thanet
Kent
CT12 4JB
01843 821 628
www.raymentwire.co.uk
Workshop open: Mon – Fri 8.30 – 4.30
Sat by appointment

With origins dating back to the early seventeenth century, the gossamer airiness, the delicate laciness and swirliness, complete and utter 'fairyness' of wirework reached its apogee with the Victorians and Edwardians, whom it completely entranced. They used it to all sorts of practical and purely decorative effect in their gardens and conservatories, its tracery outlines complementing the natural forms of precious, newly introduced plants. Fashions change, however, and rust eventually melts things into oblivion, so very few originals remain intact. The earliest extant material invariably consists of shop dummies and display racks made in France between the 1860s and the early part of the twentieth century by prison labour. 'Antique' gardenalia is rarely a fraction of the age claimed, so unless you're a serious collector you're better advised by far to buy brand new wirework from one of the handful of people scattered around the globe still skilled in the craft. One such man is Ron Rayment, who has been a leader in the field for more than 20 years.

At his workshop in a rural Kentish village, hand-formed mild steel frames are galvanized by hot dipping before nimble fingers spin a network of ornament all around and across them. The finished pieces are then treated further to build up a rich patina – all will enjoy a far longer lifespan than any of their ancestors.

Customers are welcome to visit and see what's on offer, but demand is high so if you want to buy from stock I suggest you visit during winter or early in spring before everything is snapped up in the frenzy of summertime. Many designs are based on engravings in nineteenth-century gardening books, others are Rayment's original creations. Because of the nature of production you can also arrange for items to be made up to your specific requirements.

Pieces are exported to the four corners of the earth, and they have found especial favour in Japan as well as across the Atlantic. Americans have a weird but lovely phrase which I think is especially apposite to the work that's on offer here – 'heirloom quality'.

RHS

PRODUCTS INCLUDE:
Aprons
Baskets
Botanical art
Books – new, second-hand, antiquarian
Boots
Bulbs
Engraved glass
Fertilizers
Flower arrangers' sundries
Forks and spades
Hand tools
Plant labels
Plant ties
Plants
Secateurs
Seeds
Stationery
Twine

RHS London Flower Shows
Lawrence Hall (Greycoat Street)
Lindley Hall (Vincent Square)
London
SW1
020 7649 1885
www.rhs.org.uk
Open: telephone for forthcoming dates

On Wednesday, 7 March, 1804, at Hatchard's Bookshop, 187 Piccadilly, a handful of eminent men in their fields held a meeting with 'the purpose of instituting a Society for the Improvement of Horticulture'. It was the birth of the Royal Horticultural Society.

Two centuries on, the RHS has around 324,000 members. Amongst numerous other activities it publishes books and magazines, it runs four glorious gardens for the purposes of research, conservation, training and education (there are some great shops there too), and it organizes flower shows all around the UK – the best known being Chelsea and Hampton Court, followed by BBC Gardeners' World Live, Malvern and Tatton Park. But the RHS has a secret, right at the heart of its Westminster headquarters. And you might like to cut yourself a piece of the action...

In autumn, winter and spring, for two days each month, there's a flower show on the premises. National plant societies hold competitions here. Botanical art and photography are exhibited. Specialist nurseries sell the choicest of their stock in front of beautiful seasonal displays. There's also a wide selection of gardening products and accessories on offer. If ever proof were needed of what a lovely bunch of people gardeners are, this is the place to come. Dukes and tired commuters, wonky old gentlemen and sprightly young designers are on an equal footing here. Ladies up from the country, retired women gardeners and newly wed girls down from the office rub shoulders and chat like old friends. The nurserymen are as happy to chat and give advice as to get around to selling. The booksellers and sundries merchants really know their stuff. I adore this place, I've loved it since I was a penniless student.

Now read this carefully, I will say it only once: there is an admission fee if you don't belong to the RHS, but members may bring a guest in free of charge on the second day of each show. As you join the stream of enthusiasts walking towards the door, do remember what lovely people gardeners are.

RHS Gardens to visit: Harlow Carr, Crag Lane, Harrogate, Yorkshire HG3 1QB, 01423 565 418

Hyde Hall, Buckhatch Lane, Rettendon, Chelmsford, Essex CM3 8ET, 01245 400 256

Rosemoor, Great Torrington, North Devon EX38 8PH, 01805 624 067

Wisley, Woking, Surrey GU23 6QB, 01483 224 234

SALLY ANDERSON

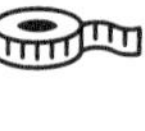

PRODUCTS:
Hand-decorated tile designs for indoors & out

Sally Anderson (Ceramics) Ltd
Parndon Mill
Harlow
Essex
CM20 2HP
01279 420 982
www.sally-anderson.co.uk
Open: Mon – Fri by appointment

The design and production studios of this specialist company are housed in a picturesque old flour mill on a vast expanse of river. This waterside location is particularly apt, as tile artist Sally Anderson is best known for her large-scale murals around swimming pools. Both theatrical and practical, the work on offer here, much of it *trompe l'oeil*, is like nothing you will have come across before.

Carefully following original designs, the close-knit team hand decorates tile after tile, section after section, to build up complex panoramas of tropical jungles, ancient ruins, landscape gardens and rolling countryside. Millionaire rock stars in their private pools and clients of exclusive hotel spas have long appreciated the skill involved. On the domestic front it has always been possible to splash out on schemes for bathrooms and kitchens. Only recently though has there been the opportunity to enjoy some of this magic out of doors – and without it costing the earth.

A series of cameo landscapes for frost-proof tiles has been created with the small urban garden especially in mind. These 900 x 800 mm panels make wonderful focal points, whether enlivening tired old walls or sprucing up the sides of garages and sheds. And

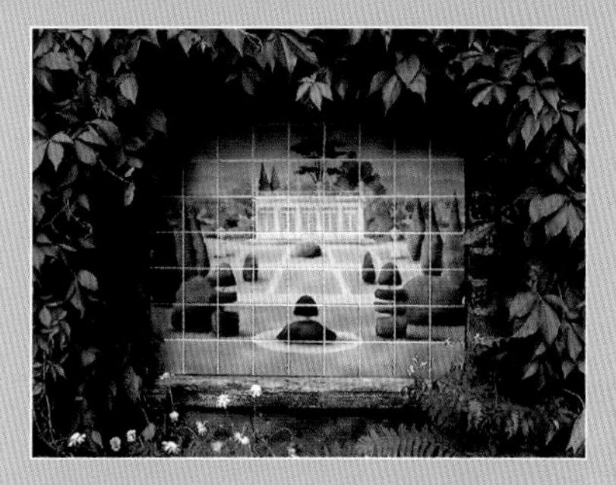

because the murals all have a distance and depth far beyond the picture plane, there's an illusion of extra space.

There's a Tropical Island Seascape with palm trees fringing a glistening beach and with windsurfers in the lapping waves. The colonnade dotted with statues in Roman Ruins gives a wonderful perspective on the past. In the Mediterranean Scene your eyes are first drawn up the steps to a sun-drenched villa before being cast down to the sandy bay below then off to the mountains way inland. Then again, you might opt for the gentle harmonies of the view towards an orangery in an English Topiary Garden.

The stained-glass vibrancy of the tiles, achieved through the suspension of natural minerals in a traditional glaze, is difficult to convey in words. Likewise, the tonal changes — from full-bodied and bright in the foreground to soft and muted in the background – are hard to imagine until you've seen them first hand. A visit to the showroom will help make up your mind, and in less than a month a blank set of tiles will have been transformed into an object of beauty ready for permanent installation (and long-term admiration) in your garden.

STUBBINGS THE GARDEN SHOP

Stubbings The Garden Shop
Market Place
Burnham Market
Norfolk
PE31 8HF
01328 730 668
www.stubbingsgardenshop.co.uk
Open: Mon – Sat 10 – 5

Just a salty sea breeze away from the glorious north Norfolk coastline, with more sun and much less rain than the rest of the country, the Burnhams consist of seven interrelated medieval parishes of which Burnham Market is the linchpin. Long rows of characteristic brick-and-flint cottages and handsome Georgian houses line the perimeter of its impeccably maintained green and market place, and you can't help but think of vicarage teas, village cricket matches and Miss Marple-type murder mysteries as you admire the scene. Not, I hasten to add, that there's anything sinister about the place. It is the archetypal chocolate

PRODUCTS INCLUDE:
Adirondack chairs
Barometers
Basketware
Bird boxes
Bird-song recordings
Crockery
Game crowns
Hammocks
Hazel & willow ware
Ironwork
Jewellery
Jigsaw puzzles
Lanterns
Playing cards
Pots & planters
Teak plant tags
Trelliswork
Trugs
Wall plaques

box/biscuit-tin lid English village fantasy come true. No wonder that there's a healthy influx of weekenders and tourists to top up the thriving local community. No wonder that the shopping here, which has to suit a wide clientele, is exceedingly good.

Mike Stubbings opened his garden shop here in 1998, and business has flourished. Originally a house, there's a front room, a back room, a courtyard and a stable full not only of all sorts of lovely things for the garden, but a wide variety of well-designed goods on a gardening theme such as jigsaws, prints and jewellery. Business has been good and plans are now afoot to develop it further by incorporating a garden *per se* where people can sit and admire even more gorgeous products.

Mike goes to inordinate trouble to source quality items from small companies both in the UK and abroad, and the work of local Norfolk craftsmen is well represented. With over three-hundred suppliers on his books, there are many things here you'd be hard pushed to find anywhere else, so it's well worth making the trip. The only question is whether you come to Norfolk with a view to taking in Stubbings, or whether you visit Stubbings with a view to taking in Norfolk.

THE URBAN GARDENER

PRODUCTS INCLUDE:
Aprons
Beetle boot-jacks
Bird feeders
Bird tables
Boules
Children's gardening equipment
Footwear
Fountain heads
Galileo thermometers
Hammocks
Miniature scarecrows
Nesting boxes
Plant stakes
Sundials
Terracotta gnomes
Unusual herb seeds
Wildflower seed mats
Wind chimes & mobiles
Wooden hedgehog homes

The Urban Gardener
18 Market Square
Bromley
Kent
BR1 1NA
020 8313 3644
Open: Mon – Sat 9–5.30, Sun 11 – 5

What I find fascinating about so many of the shops and businesses I've visited is that they have grown out of a genuine personal need. By which I don't mean the call for ready cash – believe me, the path to riches isn't paved with garden slabs – but a desire for something really special. Some people have gone into manufacturing in order to create products they couldn't source any other way; others have got into retailing to set up precisely the kind of establishment they'd like to walk into as customers. Just such a person is Chris Pluck of The Urban Gardener.

While bringing up her family, whenever Christmas, her birthday, Mother's Day or her wedding anniversary loomed, Chris would be asked what she wanted as a present. The answer would invariably be 'something lovely for the garden'. Trouble was, there was nowhere nearby to get it from, whatever 'it' might be.

Finally, the penny dropped and Chris's businessman husband had the idea for a shop that she could run standing on her head. The Urban Gardener celebrated its tenth birthday in May 2003, making it one of the oldest established garden shops in the UK. As Chris laughs now, she'll end up running it from her zimmer frame.

For a specialist independent shop in a busy town centre to hold its own alongside chain retailers is a considerable achievement, especially with such large premises. The secret here lies not in competing with hard-nosed commerce, but in providing a complete and utter contrast. With classical music playing in the background and a marvellous atmosphere of space and light, The Urban Gardener is a welcome retreat from the hubbub on the surrounding streets, a place to collect your thoughts and to reflect upon the peace and tranquillity of the real outdoors.

Urban gardeners are often short on space, so Chris offers two clever pieces of outdoor furniture that fold away to nothing. There's a lightweight self-supporting hammock if suitable trees are in scant supply, and for relaxed lounging there's an incredibly comfortable rocking deckchair with a solid beech frame. To encourage animal life in town, there are bird feeders, bird tables, nesting boxes, wildflower seedmats for keeping the butterfly population afloat, and down-to-earth wooden homes for hedgehogs. Given the shop's origins, though, it's in the realm of garden decorations and gifts that it most excels. At any given moment, people of all ages and backgrounds are happily browsing for inspiration, from children looking for pocket-money presents, such as bunches of Provence lavender or fairy-topped iron plant stakes; to young couples clearly setting up home with their eye on potted herbs and ornaments like stainless-steel reflecting globes; to husbands and wives looking for that very special something, be it a copper weathervane, a bronze armillary sundial or an elegant free-standing birdhouse like a miniature dovecote. Chris has made it all so easy for them.

URBIS DESIGN

PRODUCTS INCLUDE:
Benches
Pots & planters
Rooftop planting systems

Urbis Design
City Studios
Tyssen Street
London
E8 2ND
020 7254 0601
www.urbisdesign.co.uk
Viewing by appointment

With a rigorous training in sculpture which began at the age of 16, Richard Mackness went on to teach the subject at art school for the best part of a decade. He eventually recognized an inner frustration at spending so much more time teaching than doing, and to change the focus of his life he set off for New York. 'If you're actually motivated and you really want to get things done, that's the place where they know how to do it.' Working for a company involved in the fabrication of display pieces for national museums and in casting the work of world-renowned sculptors, he gained a high level of expertise in mould making, and the envisaged one-year break grew into a fantastic six-year experience.

On returning to the UK he produced work not only for museums and visitor centres, but for film, television and theatre, theme parks and restaurants before setting up a venture entirely his own. As a confirmed city dweller Richard looked around at what was available for gardens and there was a conspicuous absence of good contemporary design both in furniture and containers. The aim of Urbis Design is to fill that void. And the pieces on offer are out of this world.

Richard's vessels instantly command the attention normally reserved for works of art. Which of course is precisely what they are, only their gallery is the modern urban space. Cast in concrete, but not at all as we know it, these strikingly original forms have much thinner walls and a far finer surface finish than you would ever have thought the medium could allow. For sheer quality and modernity, I can't help but compare them to the much sought-after bowls and vases created by Keith Murray for Wedgwood in the 1930s – yes, they're that good. An advanced version of glass-reinforced cement is used, which can be laminated for extra strength when necessary instead of being made ever thicker and thicker. Even very large planters retain an inordinate grace – which is why landscape architects are now queuing round the block to commission series of work for various prestigious commercial and residential developments in areas like Docklands. Pieces on a domestic scale can be purchased from stock though, and a visit to his studio will not only fire you with an urge to collect his planters but tempt you into buying one of his extraordinary 'JFK' benches inspired by the TWA terminal building in New York. Give them all serious consideration: they don't cost anything like as much as you'd imagine and I honestly believe they are the gardening antiques of the future.

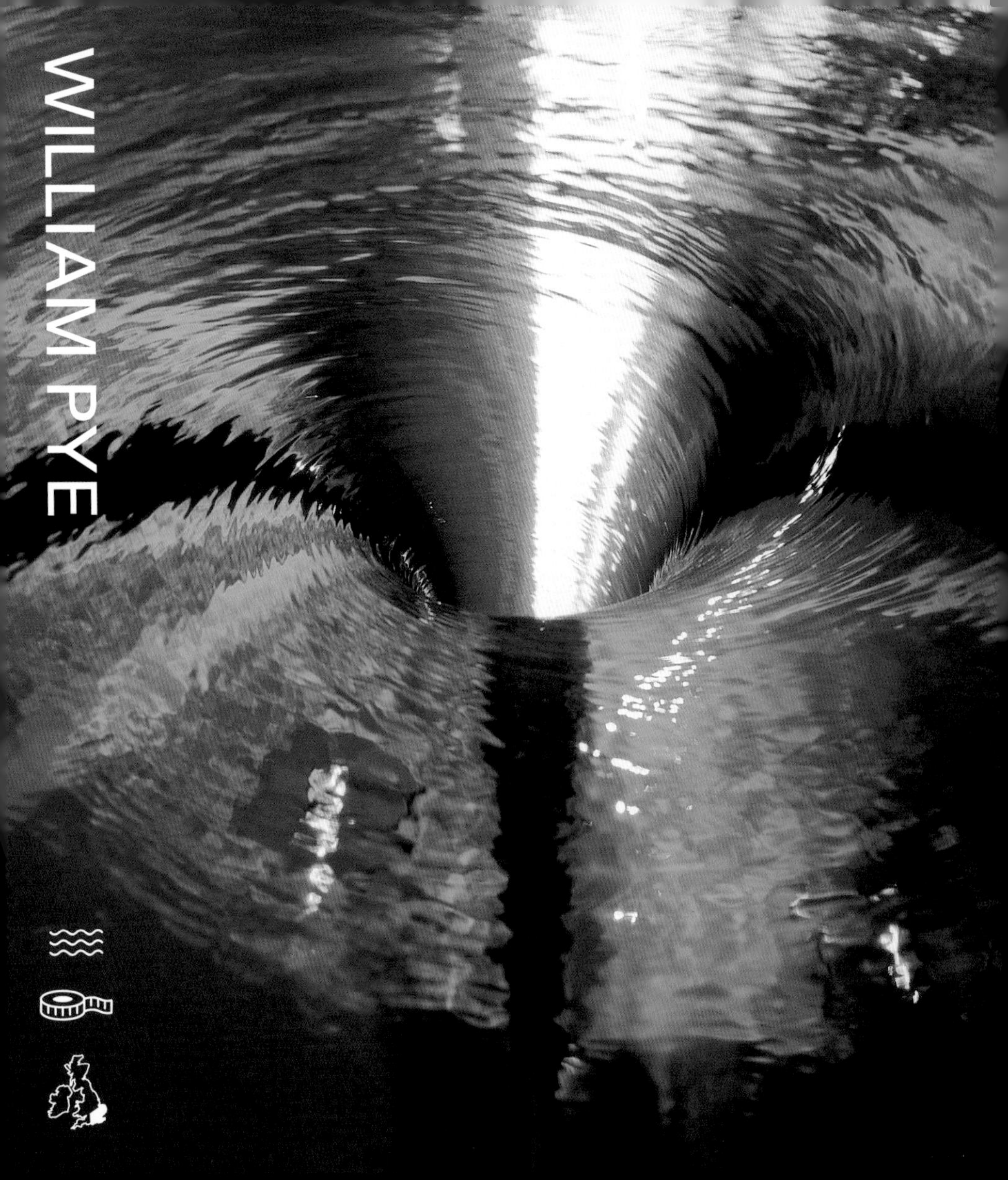
WILLIAM PYE

PRODUCTS:
seriously ground-breaking water sculpture for interior & exterior locations & for the garden

William Pye
The Studio
Rear of 31 Bellevue Road
London
SW17 7EF
020 8682 2727
www.williampye.com
Works to commission

So consummate is sculptor William Pye's mastery of the base substance water that it becomes an entirely new element in his hands. His studio is akin to an alchemist's laboratory, where constant experimentation produces truly magical effects. Broad, sheer curtains of falling water highlight its transparency. Still, dark shallows reflect the sky and the world all around. Carefully formed spouts send glass-like ropes of water streaming to the ground and high-pressure hidden jets project it upwards in smooth parabolic arcs before shaped and angled deflector cups scatter it to the winds at journey's end. Nature is harnessed to produce roll-wave effects where thin films of water flowing over sheer planes are pulled by surface tension into rhythmic patterns. Science and technology are brought into play to create massively powerful, deeply spiralling vortices which leave you hypnotized and spellbound.

Pye likes his work to be site-specific and client-oriented, so no two pieces are ever the same. Nevertheless, certain shapes and patterns recur because they have been developed to be as one with the natural properties of water; each unique creation therefore carries the distinctive William Pye 'look' while entirely coinciding with and complementing its surroundings.

Wherever you live in the UK, you will undoubtedly have seen one of Pye's large-scale installations on public display. There are giant water-clad cones and amphitheatres; clear acrylic columns holding whirlpools; transparent cubes and stainless-steel walls with gently rippling sides; mysterious stone stairways; water-topped tables of patinated bronze with cut-out silhouettes in the reflected sky; a pool where the surface is pierced with flame; and trellises of water in the air.

What you may never have seen though and, perhaps you never will unless you commission one yourself, are his exquisite smaller-scale pieces for private clients. He finds these a joy to create because of the more intimate rapport and because 'serious gardeners provide the most wonderful settings'. Why not consider taking the plunge?

It could be something in the waters at Bath, or it could be down to the cider of Devon and Somerset, but whatever it is there's no question that this part of the UK is full of fertile minds and stirring imaginations. All with a great empathy for the world around them, all producing great things for the garden.

By keeping ancient craft traditions alive and by finding new ways to apply them, people like Jason Griffiths and companies like English Hurdle are not only producing beautiful goods for the contemporary market, their land management skills are helping to preserve the delicate natural balance of the local environment. Potter Jonathan Garratt, willow sculptor Serena de la Hey and stonemason Tom Clarke are turning rough and ready materials into extraordinary works of art. Neil Wilkin is breathing new life into glass and reinvigorating the outdoor spaces where his plant forms take root. Under Sefton Whorlow's hands in the heat of the Smack Iron forge, worn-out car parts and industrial detritus turn into magical animals with spirit and soul.

SOUTH-WEST ENGLAND AND WALES

ARCHITECTURAL HERITAGE

PRODUCTS INCLUDE:
Benches & tables
Cast-bronze figures
Cast-lead statues
Chimney pieces
Columns
Finials
Fountains
Gates
Hand-carved marble figures
Limestone garden ornaments
Obelisks
Pergolas
Plinths
Staddle stones
Statues
Sundials
Terracotta figurines
Tree seats
Troughs
Urns
Weathervanes
Wellheads

Architectural Heritage
Taddington Manor
Taddington
Nr Cutsdean
Cheltenham
Gloucestershire
GL54 5RY
01386 584 414
www.architectural-heritage.co.uk
Open: Mon – Fri 9.30 – 5.30
Sat 10.30 – 4.30

How many businesses do you know with an on-site helipad? The Puddy family's vast collection of rare and important antique garden ornaments is a major international resource for designers and high-profile private clients who literally drop in from all over the world to see what's on offer. A pair of seventeenth-century limestone sea horses from an Italian villa are among the gems at the very top end of the market. Originally forming the central feature of a large fountain now no longer in existence, the web-footed fish-tailed stallions were rescued and kept in storage since the time of the Second World War until purchased by Architectural Heritage. Another extraordinary piece of history hails from a country house in Essex: a massive Georgian sandstone column with a hexagonal top, each side is fitted with a sundial and then the whole lot is topped with a weathervane. Among smaller pieces are classically inspired figures in stone and lead, urns, fountains and garden seats. There are a thousand or so items on display in two acres of grounds, and assorted galleries, barns and outbuildings housing chimney-pieces, fireplaces and entire panelled rooms.

In addition, the company has an exclusive collection of historically accurate garden ornaments hand-carved in natural limestone after antique originals. The Country House Archive includes temples, Renaissance, neo-classical, Georgian and Baroque seats, obelisks, plinths and three styles of wellhead. There are further pieces in artificial stone including a fawn, a hare and a heron, various fountains and an enigmatic sphinx.

As if all this weren't enough, there are modern castings in bronze of a figure of Narcissus found in the excavations at Pompeii, of the seated Mercury discovered in 1758 at Herculaneum and of Donatello's David commissioned by Cosimo de Medici for his palace in Florence. There are cast-lead statues too, and following the discovery of an archive of original plaster moulds, biscuit terracotta figurines of the kind found in eighteenth- and nineteenth-century French gardens. Most exquisite of all are hand-carved reproductions in marble of Greek and Roman originals – but if you have to ask the price, then I'm afraid you can't afford them.

THE CELTIC GARDEN

PRODUCTS INCLUDE:
- Cachepots
- Flowerpots
- Garden edging
- Installation pieces
- Tables
- Urns
- Wall planters

The Celtic Garden
Bron Meillion
Tregeiriog
Llangollen
LL20 7HT
01691 600 259
www.celticgarden.co.uk
Open: Wed – Sun 10 – 5
Please telephone before visiting in winter

First things first: the Celtic Garden, or Gardd Geltaidd, of Sylvia and Trefor Jones really is a garden. Each piece of furniture or sculpture there is either an expression of a theme or idea derived from early Welsh and Irish literature or is inspired by an ancient Celtic artefact. More than that, the route that visitors take through the garden represents a spiritual journey through life.

Perhaps the most characteristic piece in the garden is the Calan Gaeaf planter, a head looking two ways inspired by finds in Bronze Age archaeological sites, which pre-date the Roman invasion and subsequent introduction of the deity Janus. While Janus gave his name to the month of January, the Calan Gaeaf represents the Celtic new year which begins at the end of October, as midnight or winter dawns. The human head holds both memory and perception, so looks to the future in the light of past experience.

Another work by Sylvia is a trough featuring three adjacent faces merging one into the other. This triple goddess represents not only the waxing, full and waning moon but in human terms, the maiden, the mother and the hag. Sylvia has also created a series of standing stones carved with Pictish animal reliefs, and stepping stones to be laid in pathways or across shallow water, representing flux and stasis, the interdependence of opposite elements, and the four seasons.

Hand-moulded in concrete or carved directly out of the material when barely set, Sylvia's work has a deliberately crude, primitive, elemental edge that is magnetically attractive. Meanwhile, Trefor crafts furniture out of Welsh oak and other hardwoods containing visual references to the images in folk tales, to the decorations on medieval manuscripts and, in the case of his Scriptoria table and bench, to the very letter forms themselves. He also creates copper-bound wooden tubs and buckets styled on containers found in digs at Glastonbury.

Last but not least, Sylvia and Trefor also hold workshops and write on the Gardd Geltaidd concept.

CENTRE FOR ALTERNATIVE
TECHNOLOGY

PRODUCTS INCLUDE:
- Biological pest controls
- Bird boxes
- Bird feeders
- Books & information sheets
- Butterfly boxes
- Compost bins
- Ladybird nests
- Lanterns
- Natural wood preservatives
- Nesting & roosting boxes
- Organic paints
- Patio spotlights
- Recycled glass mosaic tiles
- Root-training systems
- Solar panels
- Solar-powered fountains
- Solar-powered garden lights
- Windchimes
- Wind gauges
- Wind turbines
- Worm composters

SERVICES INCLUDE:
- Short courses
- MSc in environmental architecture
- Mail-order

Centre for Alternative Technology
Machynlleth
Powys
SY20 9AZ
01654 705 950
www.cat.org.uk
Open: daily 10 – 6
(or dusk if that is earlier)

The Centre for Alternative Technology (CAT) is concerned with 'the search for globally sustainable, whole and ecologically sound technologies and ways of life'. The seven-acre ecological park has renewable energy systems on display, ecologically conscious buildings, farm animals, wildlife areas, ten areas devoted to different aspects of gardening, a wholefood vegetarian restaurant and a shop. A number of staff and volunteers live permanently on the site, so it is very much a working demonstration of sustainable systems in action. If you get together a group, they have two holiday Eco Cabins where you can experience the lifestyle yourself.

What is alternative and experimental one day can become part of mainstream theory and practice the next. Cynics might dismiss the 'alternative' label as shorthand for 'woolly-minded', but there's a lot of hard science going on at CAT, and when they say 'technology' here they jolly well mean it.

CAT offers a range of professional consultancy services; it runs short courses on solar water heating systems, reed filtration systems, wind power, sewage composting, hydro-electricity, organic gardening and eco-friendly house construction; it even offers an MSc in Environmental Architecture.

The books and products on sale reflect a very serious intent, although there are plenty of fun items too. There are books on science, organic gardening and recycling for children, along with various craft and activities kits. There's instruction on organic gardening and a wide range of garden crafts, including dry-stone walling and willow weaving. As well as technical and construction manuals for professionals, products include high-specification rechargeable solar lights such as fluorescent strips and spotlights for the patio, marker lights to line pathways and accent lanterns for garden decoration. There's even a solar-powered fountain. You can buy a highly efficient worm composter, complete with worms; various nesting and roosting boxes for garden-friendly insects; and biological controls to keep down those that are pests. There are also cloches, fleeces, newspaper-pot kits and root-training systems for seedlings and cuttings. All in all, some very sound and sensible stuff, and if you can't shop in person then the CAT catalogue for buying green by mail is an excellent alternative.

THE CHILDREN'S COTTAGE COMPANY

The Children's Cottage Company
The Sanctuary
Shobrooke
Crediton
Devon
EX17 1BG
01363 772 061
www.play-houses.com
Viewing by appointment

The term 'Wendy house' only entered our language early in the twentieth century in consequence of the enormous success of J. M. Barrie's Peter Pan, but purpose-built fantasy retreats for children have enchanted families in Britain for at least four-hundred years. They answer the need all youngsters have for dens and secret places away from adult eyes, where they are free from the ordinary constraints placed on them in the home. They give parents the reassurance of having provided their offspring with a safe environment for creative play – though, quite coincidentally, some very welcome peace and quiet comes as an integral part of the package.

Catrina Finlay's happy memories of the old Victorian playhouse in her grandparents' garden meant that something just as lovely had to be found for her daughter. Alas, she and husband Robin Bruce spent many fruitless hours driving to toyshops and garden centres in vain pursuit of their dream before finally realizing that the only way to get what they wanted was to design and construct it themselves. A friend of theirs who was an interior designer so admired the finished article that she persuaded them to make another one for her. After this, interest snowballed, the couple suddenly found that as well as a growing family they had a great business opportunity on their hands, and since 1994 The Children's Cottage Company has produced the most amazing playhouses imaginable.

Clients can have a classic country cottage in any of three sizes, with or without a veranda, in any colour they wish, and it can be thatched, tiled, covered in cedar shingles or be smartly roofed in slate. There's a Regency Gothic playhouse as a rustic retreat. A timbered Tudor yeoman's cottage can be finished in conventional black and white or in the style of homes in your area – pink and natural wood for Suffolk; yellow clay for Essex. A perfectly scaled Queen Anne house in a handsome brick finish comes with working sash windows and a staircase leading to an upstairs gallery. The company will even make a miniature copy of your very own home or produce a fairytale extravaganza of a gingerbread house. And all houses can be kitted out with miniature desks, chairs, tables, stools and beds.

To make the playhouses more exciting still as children grow older, they can be given a whole new lease of life by being lifted into treetops or raised off the ground on stilts. Platforms can be added, along with swings, slides, climbing walls, cargo nets and rope-ladders (which are also available separately), can all be swiftly incorporated. What more could you wish for?

PRODUCTS INCLUDE:
Child-sized furniture
Playhouses
Play systems
Tree houses

DERWEN GARDEN CENTRE

Derwen Garden Centre
Guilsfield
Nr Welshpool
Powys
SY21 9PH
01938 553 015
www.derwengardencentre.co.uk
Open: Daily 10 – 6
except Tue 2 – 6

'People like coming here for the atmosphere and because our emphasis is on looking pretty and having friendly staff.' So says Kathy Joseph, who set the whole place up. Not only is there no disagreeing with her, chain garden centres would do very well indeed to take a leaf out of her book. There's a licensed restaurant, a maze, a vast range of interesting outdoor plants and an attractive greenhouse full of unusual indoor and conservatory plants. There's also a lot of non-plant shopping to be done, with quality and value for money very much prime considerations: 'When I'm buying I try to hunt around for either a really good price or for something really different.'

That ethos certainly strikes a chord with me. As a Yorkshireman with Scottish ancestry I like a bargain when I can find it, but I've got common sense enough to know that where some things are concerned you only get what you pay for. A good case in point where Kathy is concerned are those terracotta heaters and ovens that come from Mexico. Truth to tell, they're not always as good as they could be. At Derwen Kathy's pragmatic approach means you can buy seconds of these as cheap planters – in which role they're perfect – but the only items sold as stoves are the UK-made Bushman burners which are well worth the extra cost for the many years of wear they'll give you. Another case: Kathy imports Chinese, Vietnamese and Pakistani pots to get the pick of the stock and to pass her savings on to her customers.

Kathy has two types of client to please. From Easter to September Powys sees a vast influx of tourists. Gardeners come not only to visit the nearby hanging terraces of the early Baroque masterpiece of Powis Castle run by the National Trust, they also come to visit the Joseph family's own Dingle Garden and Dingle Retail Nursery which are both just five minutes' drive up the road. In the autumn and winter months, visitors are mostly locals looking for a morning's or afternoon's distraction and a spot of retail therapy. Everyone, Kathy is happy to note, leaves in a state of well-being.

PRODUCTS INCLUDE:
Arbours
Benches
Bushman burners
Cachepots & vases
Candles & flares
Chinese, Vietnamese
& Pakistani pots
Gardeners' gifts
Hammocks
Homewares
Jewellery
Lanterns
Rustic arches
Salt-glazed
stoneware & English
terracotta pots
Solar water features
Statuary
Weathervanes
Windchimes

ENGLISH HURDLE

PRODUCTS INCLUDE:
Arbours
Bower seats
Children's forts & wigwams
Conical plant supports
Fan-shaped plant supports
Gates
Hurdles
Living willow columns
Living willow hedging rolls
Living willow play tunnels
Living willow trellis
Maypole plant supports
Rope ladders
Rose arches
Twisted trees
Withy wreaths

English Hurdle
Curload
Stoke St Gregory
Taunton
Somerset
TA3 6JD
01823 698 418
www.hurdle.co.uk
Open: Mon – Fri 8 – 5
Sat 9 – 1
Other times by appointment

Willow has been growing on the Somerset Levels ever since the sea retreated over six-thousand years ago, and traditional methods of willow cultivation and weaving dating as far back as the Bronze Age are still in use there today. Where withy shelters and animal folds were once everyday necessities, today's willow structures are fashionable yet sympathetic accessories in gardens of all styles. Where a traditional English country garden might be subdivided by hurdles, arches and gateways, a suburban plot might be enlivened by a safe and attractive play tunnel for children, and a contemporary urban courtyard might feature potted willow trees with woven stems echoing indoor specimen plants of *Ficus benjamina*.

Annually coppiced from wetland willow beds, the withies are an entirely natural and infinitely sustainable resource. Absolutely no fertilizers are required, and well-managed beds are welcome havens for wildlife including rare birds and otters. While the use of some natural products in gardening – peat in particular – raises highly contentious issues, there is no question whatsoever that by supporting the willow industry you are contributing significantly to the preservation of the UK's ancient, rich rural heritage.

Nestling at the heart of a Site of Special Scientific Interest, Nigel Hector and his son James are the third and fourth generation of their family to grow and weave willow. Directing their ever-growing business from the farmhouse bought by Nigel's father, English Hurdle is now a significant local employer. Here, the complexities of nature and the processes of production mean that no machine can ever replace the care of the woodsman or the patience of the craftsman. Besides having a wide range of standard products, including living willow structures which root into the ground, the hands-on approach of English Hurdle means they can easily make up special orders and commissions. Not only that, when the occasion demands they can travel to your door and weave large-scale pieces in situ.

GARDEN ART

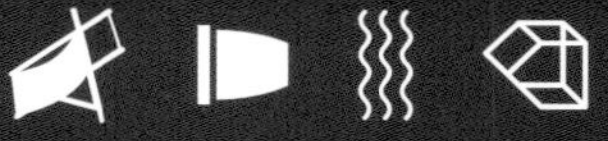

PRODUCTS:
Extraordinary
garden objects both
made & installed

Garden Art
Wilbur House
Middle Leazes
Stroud
Gloucestershire
GL5 1LG
01453 756 361
www.gardenart.co.uk
Works to commission

Gardens are magical and inspirational places. Sometimes they cry out for some unique installation to fit in with the surroundings, and sometimes gardeners want something specifically suited to their lifestyle or philosophy. Often, professional designers or private individuals will have a great idea for a garden project, but for want of the appropriate package of technical expertise and practical skills, the dream never becomes a reality. Recognizing a very real need in the gardening world, James Showers and Michael Renecle set up Garden Art to solve this problem by taking all responsibility for production and installation upon themselves. 'We encourage people really to go for it; we help them shape and refine their ideas, safe in the knowledge that we will make them work. It's about tapping into what they see, what they imagine, what they know would be wonderful.'

A cedar gateway produced under supervision of the Shinto priesthood required a sanctification ceremony around the living tree before it could be felled for its timber, and advice had to be sought from the Keeper of Japanese Antiquities at the British Museum. A commission to construct a green oak and bamboo 'Moon Gate' for a garden at Hampton Court Flower Show left the designer free, after completing the plans, to focus on other aspects of the build. An apparently simple request for a stainless-steel brazier in the ground in the shape of a crescent moon actually called for a submerged air pipe surfacing some distance away to enable the fire to draw. You or I mightn't have thought of that. Garden Art did.

When highly specialist work is called for, James and Michael have a wider network of craftsmen and artists to call on, which means that a single project can happily channel together such diverse elements as laser-cut steel, laminated wood, cast bronze, even specially curved glass. As James says: 'We can make almost anything, and that makes life really exciting.'

THE GARDEN STORE

The Garden Store
67 Fore Street
Salcombe
Devon
TQ8 8BU
01548 844 449
Open: Winter Mon – Sat 10 – 5
Sun 11 – 4
Summer Mon – Sat 10 – 6
Sun 11 – 5

When the sun is out, the tide is up, and there are sailing boats on the water, Salcombe and its surroundings are too picturesque for words. A wide and irregular valley stretches far inland here. A ria and not an estuary because it is flooded by the sea rather than fed by a river, it forms a vast natural harbour off the English Channel. The shores are awash with little sandy bays, with secluded cliffs and smugglers' caves, with wooded hillsides dipping down to winding creeks. A magnet for UK and continental yachtsmen, it is the kind of tourist destination that people hug to themselves as a secret. The climate is exceptionally mild. Enormous palms and towering great cordylines are everywhere; lemon trees, myrtles and agaves grow outdoors all year round.

Born and bred in the area, her father a world champion sailor and her grandfather a boatbuilder, Sally Hosking clearly adores the place. When, in 1997, the lease came up on a shop she fondly remembers from childhood, she leapt at the opportunity to run a business here. What was once a bookshop, a stationers and printers, and in latter years a gallery, is now a tranquil haven for gardeners.

Luxurious l'Occitane soaps and freshly cut flowers in elegant vases gently scent the air, sunshine streams in through the tall plate-glass windows and through the unusual foyer. Everything is calm, everything is beautiful, everything is handsomely displayed, and there's something here for everyone.

There's the very best in English and French wirework to choose from. There are Burmese barbecues and high-tech fish smokers. There are the most extraordinary ornamental chickens to carry away under your arm and fantastic sundials to commission. Chaps can buy hats, tableware, baskets and fancy wellies for the women in their lives. The girls can buy their boys toys like mechanical fly-swatters, hammocks and galvanized weather instruments. Children can be given sets of quoits, boules or croquet to play with on the beach and then to take home for the backyard. From Sally's own garden there are bunches of bay leaves, rosemary and parsley for the taking, in exchange for a donation to Macmillan Cancer Relief.

There's a generosity of spirit here that is palpable, and you'll want to come back again and again.

PRODUCTS INCLUDE:

Barbecues
Barometers & thermometers
Bird houses
Boules
Candles
Canvas aprons, bags & carriers
Clothing
Croquet sets
Enamelled wall-hangings
Fish smokers
Lotions & potions
Quoits
Secateurs & shears
Seeds for children
Sundials
Tableware
Terracotta pots
Trugs
Vases
Willow baskets
Wirework

JACQUELINE
EDGE

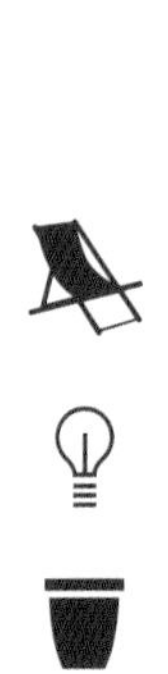

PRODUCTS INCLUDE:
Bamboo cloches
Bamboo fences & screens
Bamboo furniture
Bamboo lanterns
Bamboo planters
Benches & chairs
Grass brooms
Orchid boxes
Rush brooms
Steamer chairs
Terracotta barbecues & balticues
Terracotta pots & urns

Jacqueline Edge
The Old Barns
Manor Farm
Chilmark
Wiltshire
SP3 5AF
01722 717 800
www.jacquelineedge.com
Open: Mon – Fri 9 – 5
Sat 10 – 6

1 Courtnell Street
London
W2 5BU
020 7229 1172
Open: Mon – Sat 10 – 6

A practising solicitor who returned to university to retrain in design as a radical career change, Jacqueline Edge sums up the appeal of the exquisite creations in her shops. 'In a lot of our products we've taken elements of Eastern design but we've refined them and made them more palatable to Western tastes. While some things are authentic Burmese, Cambodian or Vietnamese designs, others are entirely our own, and others still are a fusion of the two. I think Eastern design can at times be a bit too fussy and ornate for the Western mind, so if, for example, I've seen something in a traditional Burmese style I might say well, let's take off some of the pattern, and let's make the lines a bit straighter. This way our products have a flavour of the East but they will still sit well in a contemporary UK setting.'

Many of Jacqueline's products are not only very attractive, they're incredibly useful too. She supplies a lot of garden designers direct, and she acts as a wholesaler to a great many garden stores; the feedback they give is invaluable. If designers want wider-mouthed or deeper pots, she'll see what she can do; if one style of barbecue does well in the shops, she'll look into producing others that do different jobs.

The charcoal-burning terracotta barbecue comes in two sizes and heats rapidly to a high and even temperature – it can be used as a tandoor oven when its lid is put on. The balticue cooks as an open barbecue, as an oven, and a wok on the top can be used for slow simmering. The dual-purpose fish barbecue can be used with coals as a cooker or alternatively it can be used with candles as a food warmer at table. There's a wide assortment of glazed and unglazed terracotta pots, bamboo furniture aplenty, as well as pillows and cloches. There are candles and coils of incense, teak benches and steamer chairs too.

Admirers of Jacqueline's work like to keep her name under wraps – well, now the secret's out. Track her down in deepest Wiltshire, or if you're in London, she's also got a lovely little showroom off the main retail drag in Notting Hill. And everybody's welcome.

JASON GRIFFITHS

Jason Griffiths
PO Box 9
Totnes
Devon
TQ9 5FN
07971 921 676
Works to commission

A City & Guilds qualified carpenter by profession, Jason Griffiths went on to learn the craft of the under-woodsman during the recession-hit early nineties. Under the aegis of a Devon-based charity he spent precious time with old boys, for whom the coppicing of woodlands and the creation of country furniture using only the simplest tools had been a way of life. The idea was to pass on their dying art to a select few apprentices so that it would be born anew.

For Jason, in his secluded barn far off the beaten track, the whole point of his work is that it's completely renewable. He's using indigenous material which regrows when cut, and in the process he's revitalizing woods that have been lying dormant or dying almost since the Second World War. Coppiced woodland is cut on a cycle to promote the growth of strong, straight stems. The hazel used for fencing hurdles is cut on a seven- to ten-year cycle. The willow cycle is much shorter, while that for chestnut can last up to 25 years, so it is important that each generation of woodsmen does some groundwork for the next to inherit. There's another dimension too, Jason claims: 'Once you cut, all the wildlife comes back, the dormice, the butterflies – the whole thing goes hand in hand.'

PRODUCTS INCLUDE:
Beds
Hazel hurdles
Indoor furniture
Rustic benches & tables

The big gnarled hazel stems in derelict coppices have to be cut right back in order to promote fine straight regrowth. Rather than being wasted as just so much firewood, they are destined to live on – transformed by Jason's hand into handsome pieces of rustic garden and conservatory furniture with the bark intact. Jason incorporates as many natural curves, bent knees, arms and ribs as possible into his work. His philosophy is why cut or bend wood to shape when the forms are already out there? Benches come as three, two and single seaters, and there are tables too, all held together by oak-tree nails or dowels. If they're regularly oiled, water just runs off them like a duck's back. After the process of discussing a client's requirements and agreeing a price, Jason cleaves, shapes and assembles his commissions out in the woods. That way he carries only the final product, ready for delivery by carrier, and the residue remains where it grew, to return to the earth. With little more than a bill hook, a draw knife and a shaving horse, he constructs his much-coveted indoor pieces, such as bedroom and dining furniture, from wood that is first dried and seasoned in a home-made kiln.

Disarmingly simple in appearance, Jason's work combines an elemental 'rightness' of line with a marked sophistication in construction that can come only from a master at the top of his trade – and equally from a man perfectly at ease with the natural world. What better furniture could you imagine to sit in and contemplate your garden?

JON FOX GARDEN ANTIQUES

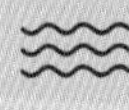

Jon Fox Garden Antiques
High Street
Moreton-in-Marsh
Gloucestershire
GL5 0AD
01608 650 714 / 325
Open: Mon – Sat 9.30 – 5.30
(Closed Tues)
Sun 11 – 4

At the head of the Evenlode Valley, between the Cotswolds and the Oxfordshire Hills, Moreton-in-Marsh is chock-a-block with history in more ways than one. An early Roman military encampment and later a Saxon settlement, it eventually came into the hands of King Edward the Confessor who included it as part of the endowment of Westminster Abbey in 1065. Under the auspices of the church it was redeveloped as a market town in the 1220s, and thanks to its position at a major cross-roads it is still thronged every Tuesday with stall-holders and shoppers who have easy access from the counties all around. Because of its long-held ties with London, Moreton not only has excellent motorway links with the capital but also a direct rail service from Paddington, and for years it has been a popular base from which the wealthier and more cultured kind of overseas tourist has explored the heart of the English countryside. It is full of charming guest houses, hotels and restaurants, and it has developed into a world-class centre for the antiques trade, becoming home to a great many internationally respected dealers.
One such is Jon Fox. A sculptor trained at the Slade, and a lecturer in design for 15 years, he has specialized in garden-related antiques since 1983 and trades from two premises on the High Street. The smaller of the two was a farm labourer's cottage, the larger a tailor's, hence the extraordinarily generous glazing in the roof, which floods the place with natural light. Here, a large indoor area painted Chinese blue and put down to Cotswold gravel makes an amazing setting for all sorts of tools, pots and cloches, for the elaborate urns and original Coalbrookdale benches for which Jon is so renowned, and for such incredible rarities as a cast-iron 'bath' for carp, an ornate glazed ceramic seat and the odd early German terracotta precursor of the garden gnome. The stock spills out of doors into the beautifully designed garden where you will find staddle stones, decorative bricks, edging tiles, chimney pots, carts and troughs of all sizes.

Be sure to drop in if you visit the nearby gardens of Hidcote and Kiftsgate. If you are really passionate about garden antiques, plan a special trip for the middle of October, when members of the Cotswold Art and Antique Dealers' Association hold an exhibition fortnight of selling shows, parties and lectures, and when Jon unveils a whole new selection of pieces for the serious connoisseur.

PRODUCTS INCLUDE:

Barrows & carts
Bell cloches
Bird-baths
Cast- & wrought-iron furniture
Chimney pots
Majolica conservatory ware
Rhubarb & seakale forcers
Statuary
Stone troughs
Sundials
Water pumps
Weathervanes

JONATHAN GARRATT

PRODUCTS INCLUDE:
Cachepots
Flowerpots
Garden edging
Installation pieces
Tableware
Urns
Wall planters

Jonathan Garratt
Hare Lane Pottery
Cranborne
Nr Wimborne
Dorset
BH21 5QT
01725 517 700
Open: daily, but phone to check

Because he operates on so many different levels at once, Jonathan Garratt's work eludes any simple classification. The courtyard of his pottery displays the sensual curves of West African and Far Eastern inspired vessels alongside more familiar-looking Mediterranean and northern European forms derived from traditional oil jars and Victorian long toms. Functional ceramic hoops replace rustic willow hurdles as edgings for large troughs and half barrels while purely decorative discs influenced by Chinese religious artefacts give a modern twist to the walls of the old farm buildings.

It is hard at first to believe that all this is the output of a single man but, as you draw back into the shadow cast by the giant chimney of Jonathan's kiln to take in the bigger picture, what emerges is a sculptor's fascination with line and fluidity. What better medium to work in, then, than clay?

Playing with shape and experimenting with the firing process is an adventure: a simple disc can be folded into a pot comfortingly shaped and coloured like an Indian samosa or into a sinister, jet-black abstraction of the American stealth bomber. Exciting product developments for Jonathan are his more recent installation works, ranging from horn-like 'Projections' for enlivening walls and fences to his 'Garden Punctuation' pieces which subvert the traditional relationship between pottery and plants.

We normally expect to see plants growing out of pots but his Garden Punctuation range is about planting clusters of ceramic forms in the garden to take on a life of their own, about knitting sculpture into the landscape. Soaring grasses look good in earth-bound pots, so why not have terracotta plumes growing out of a meadow? How about a composition of stylized musical notes to underscore a hedge, graphically evoking the birdsong and rustling leaves of a woodland? And what about a swarm of gem-coloured insect shapes darting over a pool or even some Nuba kites hovering over the flower border? It is a huge imaginative leap for outdoor pottery, yet a very natural one – out of the chrysalis comes the butterfly, as it were.

More of Jonathan Garratt's work can be seen at www.studiopottery.co.uk and at www.axisartists.org.uk/all/ref5810.htm

THE LANDSCAPE ORNAMENT COMPANY

The Landscape Ornament Company
Long Barn
Patney
Devizes
Wiltshire
SN10 3RB
01380 840 533
www.landscapeornament.com
Viewing by appointment

Michael Balston is an internationally renowned garden designer who trained first as an architect at Cambridge University before further qualifying in landscape architecture and then working on public building projects in the UK and Saudi Arabia. To increase his knowledge of horticulture and to gain experience in the realm of private garden design he joined Arabella Lennox-Boyd's London practice for a number of years before finally setting up in his own right. He has designed gardens for *Vogue* and *The Daily Telegraph* at the Chelsea Flower Show, written books and won numerous awards. Trading as The Landscape Ornament Company he has also developed a beautifully judged range of garden products.

The most immediately striking pieces are Michael's massively over-scaled sculptures of apples, pears and walnuts. Realistic and surrealistic at one and the same time, they force the onlooker's eye to make constant readjustments when darting from the ornaments to their surroundings and then back again, ultimately enhancing the appreciation of both artefact and setting. Groups of them make witty installations under the appropriate trees and single specimens have a timeless appeal. Usually cast in reconstituted Bath or Portland stone, they are also available in a mottled and shimmering glass finish.

A stately marble waterlily fountain is designed to appear as if floating on the surface of a pool, while Michael's Triton and Lion wall masks are the perfect means of introducing water into the exquisitely sculpted Shell Basin, a realistic clamshell which overflows in five frothing and sparkling rivulets.

Among the range of reconstituted stone urns and containers, you will find the especially noteworthy Wedhampton Basin with an imposing diameter of 1 m (3ft), but there is also an attractive selection of more modestly proportioned timber planters and hand-thrown terracotta pots.

The company's hand-crafted wooden benches are quite as sculptural in form as all the other pieces and make stunning focal points at the end of a walkway. The Cheverell, the Grafton, the Marden, the Sharcott and the Woodborough all come in a variety of timbers, sizes and finishes. This kind of work doesn't come cheap though, and unless you've braced yourself beforehand you may need to sit down quickly after signing your cheque.

PRODUCTS INCLUDE:
Benches
Cast stone animals
Fountains
Giant fruit sculptures
in Stone or glass
Spouting wall masks
Stone &
terracotta pots
Trellising

NATURAL DRIFTWOOD
SCULPTURES

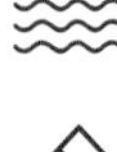

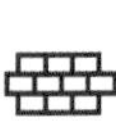

PRODUCTS:
Canadian western red cedar stumps worn away to sculptural forms

Natural Driftwood Sculptures
Sunburst House
Elliot Road
Bournemouth
BH11 8LT
01202 578 274
www.driftwoodsculptures.co.uk
Viewing by appointment

At some point or other in our lives, all of us have picked up driftwood and pebbles on a beach and been fascinated by the natural organic forms they have been shaped into by the buffeting of time and tide. In the mind's eye, a sinuously twisting length of wood can become a serpent or a sea monster; children can always see human or animal faces peeping out of more substantial pieces; the culturally inclined simply can't resist viewing them in terms of abstract or figurative art.

Pretty as our own little bits of flotsam and jetsam might be, the monumental Canadian western red-cedar stumps imported by Natural Driftwood Sculptures are in another league. In the early part of the twentieth century a number of deep river valleys in British Columbia were dammed and then flooded to create reservoir lakes producing hydro-electricity. Before this was done all the timber was felled. Over the ensuing decades successions of root boles that remained in the ground have been loosened, then finally unshackled from their earthly moorings and come floating up to the surface. Here, the constant chafing of wood on wood and the silvering effect of the sun has created wonderfully smooth artefacts which are a pleasure both to look at and to touch.

Besides using larger pieces purely and simply as free-standing sculptures, planters or water features, the driftwood can also be used to construct archways, arbours and stumperies. Straight lengths of driftwood have been split into wonderfully rustic fencing planks, while driftwood logs have been sawn into roundels which can be laid as paving on a bed of pea shingle.

Natural Driftwood Sculptures has a display centre with hundreds of items to choose from; it exhibits at major horticultural shows and it also has a select number of stockists nationwide.

NEIL WILKIN

PRODUCTS:
Glass sculpture inspired by the natural world

Neil Wilkin
Unit 3
Wallbridge Business Park
Frome
Somerset
BA11 5JY
01373 452 574
www.neilwilkin.com
Viewing by appointment

The most talked-about of all the installations at the first International Westonbirt Festival of Gardens was undoubtedly sculptor Neil Wilkin's artfully meandering line of 'Sun Catchers'. Like a breath of dandelion seeds floating down to the ground, these elegant tapering stainless-steel stems topped with 'parachutes' of glass danced across a clearing of buttercups, glistening and sparkling in the ever-changing light filtering through the trees. With some of them up to three metres tall and the majority a metre across, the combined impact of these 30 individual pieces was quite phenomenal.

Our preconceptions about glass make it seem an unlikely material for outdoor use, but once you see Neil's transparent Glass Seeds peeping out between lush foliage, once you've seen Glass Grass, his Pond Flowers, his Umbrella Trees and Dew Drops – all forms that are derived from nature – you realize that his work has a particular affinity with gardens.

'Once you put it outside, glass takes on quite different physical qualities. You can't beat sunshine for bringing out the distinctive brilliance and fragility of the material. The normal sort of dust and deposit that the weather leaves on

glass is hardly noticeable; it will always sparkle and often acts as a lens, capturing and transforming the environment around. That's what actually sells it – the surroundings, and not the glass itself.' Like many a true artist, the man seriously underestimates his own skill.

Neil's work is to be found in the Crafts Council collection and in the Victoria & Albert Museum; it has also been exhibited throughout England, in Belgium, Brazil, Germany, the Netherlands and Switzerland. He has lectured throughout Europe; he has had work commissioned by Asprey, The Elton John Aids Fountain and Thomas Goode; he also has worked with some of the leading glass studios and artists around the world. Need I say more?

THE POTTING SHED

PRODUCTS INCLUDE:
Antique tools
Artificial flowers
Bird-baths
Bird tables
Candles
Cards & stationery
Cut flowers
Footwear
Lanterns
Lotions & potions
Plants & shrubs
Pots & planters
Obelisks
Secateurs
Seeds
Statuary
Topiary shears
Trugs

The Potting Shed
Market Place
High Street
Castle Cary
Somerset
BA7 7AL
01963 350 555
Open: Mon – Sat 9.30 – 5.30

Mentioned in the Domesday Book as Cari, meaning 'the rocky hill' from the Celtic *Creag*, then recorded as Castra Cari in the early fourteenth century, Castle Cary today has many of the attributes you'd expect of a fine old Somerset town steeped in history. There's a horse-pond turned duck-pond complete with preening swans, a winding high street of Golden Ham Stone buildings, a coaching inn and a pillared market hall, there's even a quaint 'pepper-pot' lock-up for rowdies and villains. One thing in Castle Cary though is conspicuous by its absence. There's nary a castle to be seen. Long gone and long forgotten.

Clare Cooke's Potting Shed is guilty of a little false advertising too. You'd expect any shop of that name to be a small affair. Clare's enterprise, however, is large, rather splendid, and it will linger long in the memory. Née Bradley, Clare trained in horticulture at the Royal Botanic Gardens in Kew, and although she is perhaps best known as the Blue Peter gardener, she has done lots more television work besides, and has also found time to write several books aimed especially at children. Her mission and enthusiasm for gardens and for plants shines through clearly in the shop.

There's a market stall of freshly cut flowers – some of them grown in Clare's very own nursery – to catch your eye as you enter. There are lovely old garden tools alongside new Sheffield steel ones that are bright as buttons from Burgon and Ball. There are hand-forged obelisks from a local blacksmith, assorted sculptures by artists from the region, and slate-roofed bird tables from nearby Devon. There are exquisite garden lanterns and oriental pots, comfortable French wellies and a sensible selection of seeds from English growers. There are boys' toys for men, unguents for their ladies, and, as you'd expect, exciting kits and tools for kids. Outside in the courtyard, seasonally performing plants are arranged into a garden – a refreshing change from the solemn, serried ranks to be found in garden centres.

REDWOOD STONE

Redwood Stone
The Stoneworks
West Horrington
Wells
Somerset
BA5 3EH
01749 677 777
www.redwoodstone.com
Open: Mon – Fri 8.30 – 5.30
Sat: phone in advance

Redwood Stone is a second-generation family business perched up in the Mendip hills just outside the city of Wells with its twelfth-century cathedral. The carvings and traceries of this magnificent structure have inspired much of the company's work. Using only crushed natural Cotswold or Portland stone, it produces garden ornaments and architectural components that you'd be hard pushed to distinguish from stonework fresh from a mason's yard. The crisp clean lines of the classical stonework come down to the fact that the original pieces from which the moulds are made are all carved on site by traditionally trained craftsmen. After the production process each item is then hand-finished to ensure that its appearance really is as close as possible to cut stone. As director Tim Redwood says: 'Basically, we're frustrated stonemasons. We'd love to be making everything out of solid stone, but that would cost too much, and it's easier and more affordable for the customer for it to be done our way.'

An interesting recent development has been the introduction of the Reclamation Stone range. The distressed mellow finish of the gargoyles, archways, benches and planters gives an uncannily realistic sense of centuries of wear. The illusion of age is commonly sought simply by making things crudely. Tim knows this just doesn't work. 'Everything has to be carved perfectly, then aged. Weathering doesn't add lumps to stone, it removes them.' Rustic pieces like troughs will have sharp chisel marks left in, sculptures will be worked to a high surface finish. Only then are they artfully weathered as though years of wind and rain have washed away at softer layers in the bed of the rock. Balustrades, doorways, columns and quoins made this way can be combined with timber and brick to make the most wonderful follies.

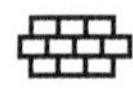

PRODUCTS INCLUDE:
Archways
Balustrades
Benches
Bird-baths
Columns
Doorways
Dragons' heads
Finials
Follies
Fonts
Fountains
Gargoyles
Lion masks
Mill stones
Obelisks
Pillars
Planters
Plinths
Troughs
Urns

SERENA DE
LA HEY

PRODUCTS:
Artworks in willow for both private & public places

Serena de la Hey
The Willows
Curload
Stoke St Gregory
Taunton
Somerset
TA3 6JD
01823 698 049
www.serenadelahey.com
Works to commission

'Willows whiten, aspens quiver,
Little breezes dusk and shiver.'
Alfred, Lord Tennyson

Willow sculptor Serena de la Hey has created garden pieces in many forms, including dogs, ducks, geese, foxes, hens, stags and wild boar. As public installations, she has also crafted huge willow figures with a dynamism and life of their own almost unimaginable in any other medium. One of these, her 12m (40ft) high 'Running Man' (pictured) is to be seen alongside the M5 motorway near the town of Bridgwater, between junctions 23 and 24. Other wicker men, now lost to the world, were part of performance and pyrotechnic displays at the Glastonbury Music Festival.

Since graduating from Falmouth School of Art and Design in 1989, Serena has achieved worldwide recognition for her innovative application of traditional materials and working methods. All of Serena's work is an exploration of movement through form and structure. 'I've always argued that willow itself is a drawing', she says. The interwoven withies making up each piece not only give it form, fleshing it out with muscle and sinew around a skeletal framework, they are also vibrant and fluid lines showing directions of movement. You sense the power and tension in the thighs of a crouching leopard, the grace of a leaping dolphin and the comical waddling of a flock of geese on the lawn.

The lifespan of outdoor willow sculptures is around eight to ten years. As natural structures in a natural setting, Serena sees their mutability as something which should be looked on positively. As they slowly fade, so their role in the garden can change. 'If they are used to fill up spaces, as introductory pieces in a new garden, then as the material becomes more fragile they can be pushed further and further back into a border, so that eventually you can allow something to grow over them.' The whole point is that you're not trying to preserve them as precious pieces, you're rather embracing the organic nature of the art.

A simple phone call or e-mail sets the commissioning process in motion. It's all rather magical when you consider that willow stems still awaiting harvest in the Somerset levels might be destined for an extraordinary sculptural flight of fancy.

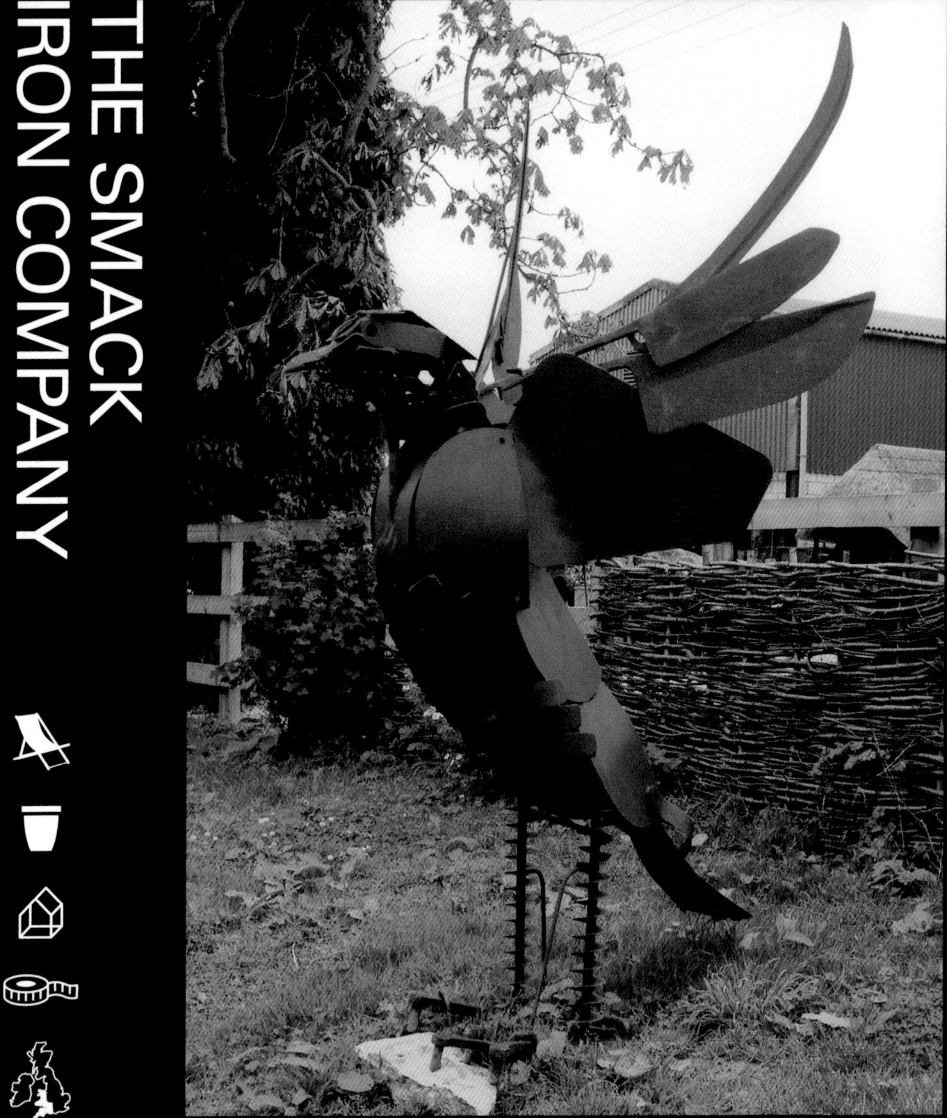
THE SMACK
IRON COMPANY

PRODUCTS INCLUDE:
Archways
Barbecues
Chairs & tables
Gates
Obelisks
Railings
Sculpture

The Smack Iron Company
The Old Forge
The Old Potato Yard
Manor Farm
Lydeway
Wiltshire
SN10 3PU
07966 495 561
Open: Mon – Sat 9 – 5

Blacksmith, metalworker, welder, artist, sculptor – it is hard to find a suitable way of describing Sefton Whorlow. None of these terms entirely fits the bill; he is all of them and more. If I had to choose a single word to sum up the man I would have to say, quite simply, that he is a visionary. Using conventional ironworking techniques he can, and indeed does, produce tables, chairs, benches, gates, railings and archways – anything in fact that you'd expect a blacksmith to turn his hands to. What marks him out as a breed apart, though, is his gift for seeing the hidden potential in scrap-metal objects and for assembling them into structures which, when they are finished, have a spellbinding wholeness, a complete and utter inevitability about them that has to be seen to be believed.

Sefton scours scrap yards, car boot fairs and farm sales for his raw materials. Old spanners, machine parts, blades from harrows, combine-harvester spikes, all are grist to his mill along with industrial sheet steel off-cuts and all sorts of detritus from car-repair shops.

His creations? Gnarled and twisting trees reaching five metres high, majestic stags and bashful does made entirely from exhaust pipes. Life-size 'woolly' sheep put together from suspension springs. Giant herons whose plumage consists of shovels and spades. Preening birds and leaping dolphins clad in shiny metal shards. A scorpion with a motorcycle fuel tank for a body. Wasps, flies and dragonflies with heavy gauge mesh for wings. There are crowing cocks, pecking hens and cats and dogs too. The Smack Iron menagerie is to be seen all about the craft centre yard adjoining Sefton's forge and if you want that extra-special something he's ready and willing to oblige, whatever your request. A man who can produce a larger-than-life chariot and horses with Boudicca at the reins won't be easily stopped in his tracks.

SURESET UK

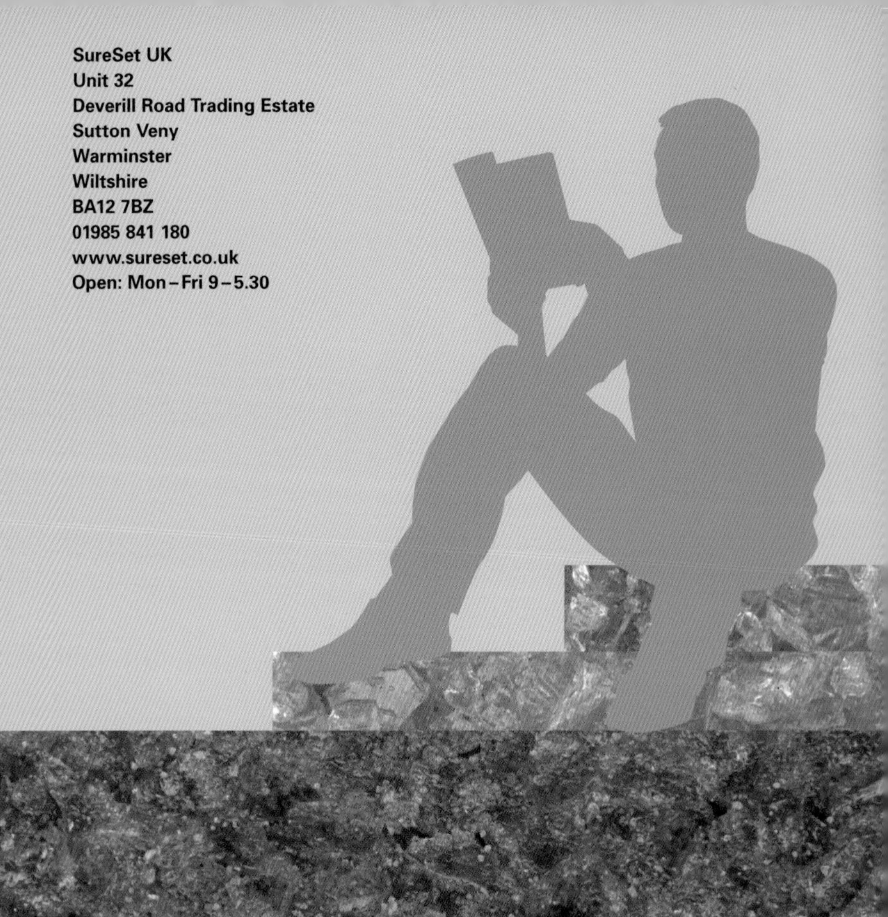

SureSet UK
Unit 32
Deverill Road Trading Estate
Sutton Veny
Warminster
Wiltshire
BA12 7BZ
01985 841 180
www.sureset.co.uk
Open: Mon – Fri 9 – 5.30

PRODUCTS:
Resin-bound surfacing in natural gravel & coloured glass

Finding an attractive surfacing for pathways, driveways and open spaces is a perennial problem for garden designers. Loose gravel, bark chippings and shingle are handsome, traditional and easy to lay, but they don't take kindly to heavy wear and tear, and they require constant grooming to look their best. The same problems apply to their hip young cousins, ground glass and tumbled slate, both of which can be treacherous underfoot. Stone slabs and brick paviours are deservedly sought-after commodities, but large expanses come with hefty price tags attached, and installation invariably involves a great deal of time-consuming preparation and labour. Asphalt is arguably a more practical alternative but it doesn't always blend in well with its surroundings and it rarely inspires the right kind of comment.

Frequently used by landscape architects in commercial developments where demands for good looks, durability and zero maintenance all carry equal weight, resin-bonded gravel is a recent innovation that is starting to make serious inroads into private gardens. SureSet is a leader in the field, and besides offering a complete planning and installation service for projects of all sizes around the UK, it also produces tailor-made kits for the DIY enthusiast.

A clear polymer is mixed on-site to bind aggregates such as gravel, ground recycled glass or marble chippings into a permanent surfacing. This means that gravel can now be used confidently in places where it was unthinkable or problematic before – such as around swimming pools, on sloping walkways and in roof gardens. Only a thin layer is required, so existing hard surfaces are easily revamped, and because differently coloured materials can be laid neatly side by side in any pattern you choose, a wealth of exciting design possibilities suddenly opens up.

If you are after a natural look, SureSet offers a large selection of gravels to fit in with your local environment; if you are after artistry, there is a vast palette of glass to draw on; and if you want something outdoors that is really off the wall the company has recently been experimenting with finely crushed lavatory pans and minced-up compact discs. Watch this space.

TOM CLARK

SERVICES & PRODUCTS INCLUDE:
Private & corporate commissions undertaken
Sculptures & carvings for gardens, patios & interiors
Weekend courses in stonecarving

Tom Clark
Hurst Barton Studio
Hurst
Martock
Somerset
TA12 6JU
01935 822 833
Studio open: Mon – Sat 10 – 5

Tom Clark started carving in 1974, originally in wood, then in stone. Working first in the yard of a monumental mason before serving out an apprenticeship in ecclesiastical masonry at Chichester Cathedral, his career took off in earnest on large-scale restoration projects at such buildings of national historic interest as Westminster Abbey, Ely Cathedral and St George's Chapel, Windsor. While the years honed his skills to perfection, Tom acquired a great love and understanding of English medieval art. In his leisure time he travelled widely in Egypt and India, where the ancient stonework he encountered made a deep and lasting impression too. All these influences converge in the sculptures and carved reliefs Tom has created over the past ten years as an artist in his own right, but they come shining through in a new and modern idiom.

His peripatetic life behind him, Tom now lives with his wife and young children in a seventeenth-century farmhouse, once used for wool combing, in the village of Hurst. He works and teaches in his studio barn; next door there is a gallery displaying his work in Portland, Bath and Cotswold stone. His pieces range from images of lions and elephants to architectural columns or stylized female figures. There are bird-baths and fountains, and there are also the most exquisite bowls. Often left with jagged edges, sometimes revealing the natural quartz crystals within, one even graces the palace gardens of an Arabian princess. Limited-edition replicas of original carvings are occasionally available in cast limestone, and wall plaques in the same material are always to be had.

For people who want to exercise their own creative talents, Tom runs weekend workshops where no more than six students at a time are given individual guidance on sketching an idea, marking out a carving, then using the appropriate tools to produce a finished sculpture to take home and enjoy.

THE WADHAM TRADING CO.

The Wadham Trading Company
France House
Digbeth Street
Stow-on-the-Wold
Gloucestershire
GL54 1BN
01451 830 308
www.wadhamtrading.co.uk
Open: Mon – Sat 10 – 5
Sun 11 – 4

High up in the Cotswolds, 'Stow-on-the-Wold, where the wind blows cold' owes its original prosperity to the wool trade. Its sheep fairs later became horse fairs, and these are still held today in the months of May and October. Boasting one of the largest and finest market places in the country, where the final skirmishes of the Civil War took place in 1646, it is now a major centre for antiques, fine arts, and all sorts of specialist shopping. In the streets, alleyways and courtyards beyond the square, there's no knowing quite what you might stumble upon.

In a shop that once housed a bakery, you'll find the Wadham Trading Company, a regular exhibitor at the Chelsea Flower Show and famous for its sturdy topiary frames. These three-dimensional steel wire structures are erected over young specimens of boxwood, privet or yew to train them into living sculpture. Not only do they support the plants as they grow, they provide the clipping guidelines for maintaining a crisp, clear outline once the intended shape has been achieved. Besides geometric forms, stock items include peacocks, swans and geese; sheep, pigs and labradors; snails, rabbits and teddy-bears. What is more, because the owners Denis and Isabelle Cox have their own country workshop with two full-time metal-workers, Wadham's can design and construct frames to any size and shape your heart might desire. Commissions have included a pair of fighting cocks for a lawn; a cat-and-mouse chase for the top of a yew hedge; there were the Alice in Wonderland figures including the Mad Hatter, the White Rabbit and the Caterpillar for Marylyn Abbott's tea garden at West Green House; there was a life-sized stallion for the Rothschilds at Waddesdon Manor. Because topiary is one of those rare elements in a garden that can be terribly smart and enormous fun, you can really afford to let your imagination run wild.

Besides a range of lead planters and statuary made to their own designs, Gothic- and Regency-style iron garden furniture and a generous selection of garden-related gifts, Denis and Isabelle also have some exclusive paintings and sculpture of animals, including race-horses, bronze March hares, and porcelain dogs by the artist Eve Pearce. There's also some fabulous Limoges.

PRODUCTS INCLUDE:

- Benches
- Books
- Chairs
- Figurines
- Lead planters
- Plant supports
- Sundials
- Tables
- Topiary frames
- Wall planters

Famous for its mines, for its potteries and its iron foundries, the Midlands has a rich industrial heritage to draw upon. Michael Hill's ornate, finely cast furniture brings the past alive and Mark Pedro de la Torre's designs put a contemporary spin on steel.

In recent years many large companies have relocated from the South-east of England both as a response to rising land prices there, and in recognition of the logistical advantages to being at the physical heartland of the UK. After going through a late twentieth-century doldrums, the economy here is buoyant once more. There is the taste and sophistication there always was, and the money has returned to back it up.

Success begets success. Jim Keeling's Whichford Pottery not only sends its wares all around Britain, it is a magnet for keen gardeners from miles and miles around. E H Thorne are world specialists in all the paraphenalia a bee-keeper could ever desire, and in consequence they ship stock to apiarists worldwide. Haddonstone's market is so vast that they now have a large manufacturing base in the US as well as the UK.

All the companies here were incredibly warm and welcoming, none more so than Hazel Hallam's Patio Planting in Lincoln. A small shop with a big personality, it really shows that good gardening – like everything else in life – comes from the heart.

MIDLANDS

ACCESS
IRRIGATION

WATERING PRODUCTS INCLUDE:
Control systems
Hose attachments & connections
Hose reels
Land-drainage systems
Leaky pipes
Liquid feeding systems
Mist-propagation systems
Pop-up sprinklers
Pump systems
Pump & tank sets
Water meters
Water tanks

OTHER PRODUCTS INCLUDE:
Blowers
Brush cutters
Circulating fans
Cloches
Greenhouse heaters
Heat mats
Hedge trimmers
Mini-greenhouses
Pressure sprayers

Access Irrigation
Crick
Northampton
NN6 7XS
01788 823 811
www.access-irrigation.co.uk
Open: Mon – Fri 8.30 – 5.00
(Closed for lunch 1 – 2)

Access Irrigation has been designing and installing watering systems for more than 30 years. Private and corporate work takes the company all around the country, from terraced backyards to rooftop restaurants, on country-estate lawns and in palace grounds. North London at the moment is a particular hot spot, but demand is growing everywhere.

Though they are often dismissed out of hand as extravagant and unnecessary, irrigation systems deserve serious consideration, and they are often well worth designing into a garden right at the outset.

Where there is only a small volume of soil, as in containers and on roof gardens, water is soon lost by surface evaporation to the wind and the sun. In such situations a thorough watering really needs to be carried out two or three times a day from spring right through to the end of summer. The moment there's not enough water for the roots of your plants to draw on, they go into a state of shock. However generously you water by hand of an evening, they may well be parched by noon the next day. Even if your plants don't give up the ghost and die, they'll always be living on a knife-edge. In an ordinary garden setting, trees, shrubs and lawns establish themselves more quickly with an irrigation system in place, and flowerbeds benefit from a more even distribution of water than can ever be achieved with a hosepipe or a can. And let's face it, even if you're the keenest, most diligent gardener around, you should still be able to take the odd holiday. It should also be pointed out that irrigation systems are a boon to elderly and disabled gardeners.

Depending on what you have in mind, Access Irrigation can help you choose a simple off-the-peg system to install yourself. Or, if you supply them with detailed garden plans they will design a purpose-built system to suit and give a quote on the equipment. Alternatively, you can arrange a site visit for a fee and the company will specify, then install, everything you need.

Callers are welcome, and besides all the irrigation supplies you'd expect, you will find high-specification mini-greenhouses, brush cutters and garden blowers, and an attractive range of good-quality outdoor lighting.

BAILEYS
HOME & GARDEN

PRODUCTS INCLUDE:

- Antique garden tools
- Barometers & thermometers
- Besom brooms
- Bird houses & feeders
- Children's gardening equipment
- Garden lines
- Lotions & potions
- Metal benches
- Picnic blankets
- Plant-labelling kits
- Recycled rubber trugs
- Tools
- Vintage wheelbarrows
- Wood oils & wax

Baileys Home & Garden
The Engine Shed
Station Approach
Ross-on-Wye
Herefordshire
HR9 7BW
01989 563 015
www.baileyshomeandgarden.com
Open: Mon – Sat 9 – 5

If you release the safety catch of your Browning whenever you hear the word 'lifestyle', now is the time to put your reflexes on hold and instead reach for your chequebook or credit card.

For more than two decades, Mark and Sally Bailey have been in the business of buying and selling beautiful things for the home and garden. Originally they dealt purely in antiques and unusual second-hand items; gradually they introduced new products of their own and sourced interesting fixtures and fittings from quality craftsmen and manufacturers to pull together a fully rounded collection of merchandise. Today, their company is a fixture itself in the firmament of interior and outdoor styling. The look on offer is a harmonious and beguiling blend of soft modernism, retro chic and rustic simplicity with a defining speck of industrial grit at the centre of the pearl. Masculine and feminine, hard-wearing but alluring, it's a style that most people want to buy into, and that families especially will adore.

On display in their Brunel-designed engine shed, the Baileys have Gothic-style cast-metal benches and softly coloured Welsh picnic blankets. There are buckets stitched from recycled rubber for carrying your hand tools around in, and there's a handsome selection of antique spades, forks, iron garden rollers and wooden wheelbarrows for heavy-duty gardening or simply for decoration. There are soothing soaks, soaps, handcreams and washes which make lovely gifts for gardeners, and for sprucing things up outdoors there are furniture-care kits with oil, steel wool and wire brushes. Their garden lighting is the kind used on old ships, made to give years of hard service, and the Baileys' bird houses, woven nesting pockets and assorted feeders will guarantee hours of daytime entertainment.

Mark and Sally's passion for good gardening products has led them to create some really well-thought-out equipment for children, including a sturdy trowel, spade and rake set, a wooden-handled bucket to bang about with and a lovely bright red watering can for helping things grow. There's a sunflower seed kit for the garden, and a window-box assortment for bringing butterflies right up to the house. And, for sweeping any mess tidily away, a miniature broom.

E H THORNE (BEEHIVES) LTD

PRODUCTS INCLUDE:
Bees & queens
Beeswax
Beeswax foundation
Books
Candle moulds
Containers,
jars & labels
Feeders
Hives
Honey blenders
Honey bottles
Honey extractors
Honey strainers
Labels
Protective clothing
Queen excluders
Skeps
Smokers
Travelling boxes

E H Thorne (Beehives) Ltd
Beehive Works
Wragby
Market Rasen
Lincolnshire
LN8 5LA
01673 858 555
www.thorne.co.uk
Open: Mon–Fri 9–5.30
Sat (Apr–Aug) 9–12
Sat (May, June and July) 9–4

'How doth the little busy bee
Improve each shining hour,
And gather honey all the day
From every opening flower!'
Isaac Watts

Thornes has been making and selling beekeeping equipment for almost a century. Besides being the centre of the universe for UK apiarists the company also serves beekeepers all around the world, not only dispensing wares but giving advice on all aspects of the craft to beginners and experienced hands alike.

The website gives a month-by-month checklist of jobs to be done, it has a diary of beekeeping events, and details of all the various beekeeping courses on offer throughout the country. Beekeeping is definitely on the increase as a hobby. It is a fascinating and environmentally friendly pursuit – and, if you're as diligent as your bees, it more than pays you back over time in honey sales. As a nation we produce only five per cent of our honey requirements ourselves, the rest is imported – an astonishing statistic for such a green and pleasant land. Thornes offers both a Standard and a Deluxe Kit for beginners, complete with a hive of your choice. The National is the most popular in the British Isles; the Langstroth, invented in 1850, is the most popular hive worldwide; the WBC, designed by William Broughton Carr at the beginning of the twentieth century, is the cottage garden classic that everyone recognizes.

Advanced and professional beekeepers might graduate to Modified Dadants Commercials, with or without Hamilton Converters, or to Smiths'. Smokers and protective veils and clothing are all to be had, along with honey-processing equipment, bottles, labels and a wide range of videos and reading matter on the subject. Sensibly, Thornes has a sideline in candle-making equipment, and on the frivolous side there are bee-related gift items including mugs, tea towels, umbrellas and – my favourite – a weathervane.

Besides the factory headquarters and the warehouse-sized shop in rural Lincolnshire, Thornes has branches in Scotland and the Home Counties, and you can also buy on-line or through the mail-order catalogue. Now, what's for tea?

PRODUCTS INCLUDE:
Bird boxes & feeders
Boules
Cloches
Copper & oak plant tags
Dibbers
Folding saws
Footwear
Garden torches
Gloves
Kneelers
Outdoor chessboards
Pruning knives
Quoits
Secateurs
Skittles
Sundials
Tool tidies
Trugs
Watering cans
Windchimes & mobiles

Begun purely as a mail-order concern in 1995 by Graham Hopper, his partner Liz Francis and her sister Alex Wall, Garden Images is now a company that operates on three different fronts. Apart from the catalogue and internet sides, Garden Images also sells from beautifully laid out stands at RHS and county flower shows and at the prestigious springtime Country Living Fair in London, and there is a gorgeous little half-timbered shop in Stratford-upon-Avon. Just a couple of minutes' walk from Shakespeare's birthplace in Henley Street, the spiritual heart of the town, it is a treasure trove chanced on as fair by tourists and chosen as true by gardeners.

The company ethos is simple. As Liz says: 'Our products, we hope, are for people who actually enjoy being in their gardens, who enjoy visiting gardens and who also enjoy working in their gardens. We just try to get them good value for money in their products.' People who see them at shows often become mail-order customers. People who were originally mail-order customers eventually track down the shop. Shop customers subsequently order on-line or from catalogues and visit them at shows. The trio are definitely on the right track.

Timeless Sussex trugs handmade to a classic design from willow and sweet chestnut come in a variety of sizes. Watering cans made since 1886 by Haws in nearby Birmingham are consistent best-sellers, the conservatory can with a long brass extension spout being especially popular. For relaxation there are sets of wooden skittles, garden quoits, boules and wildly oversized outdoor chess boards. On the wildlife front there's a wide variety of birdhouses and bird feeders, a butterfly house for caterpillars to pupate in, a hedgehog house in wood and a bug box for ladybirds. For a modern touch, there are spiralling mobiles in either wood or acrylic, flaming torches in shining stainless steel and matt-finished glass and futuristic cloches in transparent plastic. There are also Victorian-style glass and metal lantern cloches, cold-cast bronze animal sculptures by artist Suzie Marsh and tough leather gloves and waxed cotton kneelers. Whatever your taste, whatever the style of your garden, there's something to suit your image here – and to suit your pocket too.

HOLLOWAYS

PRODUCTS INCLUDE:
Benches
Bird-baths
Conservatory plants
Conservatory suites & dining furniture
Fountains
Garden antiques
Garden furniture
Pergolas
Plant stands
Pots & planters
Statuary
Summer-houses

Holloways
Lower Court
Suckley
Worcestershire
WR6 5DE
01886 884 665
www.holloways.co.uk
Open: Mon – Sat 9 – 5
Sun (April – Aug) 11 – 4

Holloways is situated in the beautiful border countryside of Worcestershire and Herefordshire that so inspired the composer Sir Edward Elgar. Close to the Malvern Hills and the Three Counties Showground, within easy reach of Great Malvern and the historic cathedral city and bone-china capital of Worcester, Holloways is one of those places that you pop into on the way to somewhere else only to realize when you get there that it is very much a destination in its own right. If you don't want to leave yourself breathless, I suggest you allow plenty of time for browsing.

The showrooms of this family business occupy two floors of a converted hop kiln and display what is probably the largest assortment of conservatory furniture you'll find under one roof in the UK. Besides traditional English Lloyd Loom suites, woven from paper on wire, there are chairs, tables and loungers in such diverse materials as banana bark, cane, iron, rattan, seagrass and willow. Some ranges come with a choice of cushion coverings included in the price, with others you have *carte blanche* to choose from hundreds of fabric books. With anything from English florals and toiles de Jouy for a country house look, to bold graphics and strong colours with a modern slant, and with serious names such as Andrew Martin, Designers Guild, Mulberry, Romo and Thomas Dare to tempt you, you'll end up with something that is not only unique but perfectly suited to your lifestyle.

In addition to the indoor showrooms, there is a glasshouse full of rare and unusual conservatory plants and there are two courtyards full of garden furniture, ornaments and architectural stonework and salvage. Holloways helpfully distinguishes old pieces from the new by reserving the front area for modern and reproduction items and the other one for antiques. I honestly wish more people did this. There are reconstituted stone fountains and pools, bronze statues large and small, lead cisterns and planters, sundials and bird-baths. Typical antique items might include stone benches, urns and figures, cast-iron seats and old farming artefacts. Sometimes, if owner Edward Holloway has come across something really special on his travels, you might also be lucky enough to find such superior reclaimed landscaping materials as cobblestones worn smooth by horses' hooves, old stone steps, patterned edging tiles, and fine dressed stonework from buildings and bridges.

HADDONSTONE

Haddonstone
The Forge House
East Haddon
Northampton
NN6 8DB
01604 770 711
www.haddonstone.co.uk
Open: Mon – Fri 9 – 5

A world-renowned manufacturer of cast stone, Haddonstone produces landscape ornaments and architectural features in three colours: white Portland, golden-yellow Bath, and a warm but muted terracotta. The stone finishes of course are those most commonly called upon for statues and structures, but the terracotta really comes into its own when used to recreate the Arts & Crafts Movement bowls and jardinières designed by Mary Watts for the Compton Pottery. Haddonstone has an immense range of products from classical temples and colonnades through to fountains, seats and ornaments from the great styles and traditions of European gardening. The distinct Arcadian range has smaller, more contemporary pieces, amongst which the spouting wall masks and the self-contained pebble bowl water-features are outstanding.

The company's show garden – not a yard, I hasten to add, but four acres of beautifully laid-out grounds with mature trees and plantings – is a joy to visit. Not only does it form the perfect backdrop for a vast number of Haddonstone creations, it allows you to see how they age and mature to complement flowers and greenery. If planted up, or put amongst foliage, near water or under trees, algae and lichens soon take hold. In dry, sunny spots the antiquing process can be hastened if you wish with a special formulation to confer age in an instant.

Lending themselves so easily to a variety of different looks, Haddonstone products are a popular choice among professional garden designers. It would be impossible to describe the entire collection, so I'll mention just a few favourites. The timber dovecote on a Tuscan-style column has just the right balance of simplicity and elegance for a smart country cottage. The octagonal Gothic jardinière is a fantastic centrepiece for the larger garden, begging for changing seasonal displays of bulbs and annuals. The imposing Versailles vase on the other hand, simply asks for a single, permanent clean-lined 'architectural' evergreen such as a cordyline or yucca, and is sure to make a fantastic statement just about anywhere.

PRODUCTS INCLUDE:
Architectural stonework
Balustrading
Baskets
Bird-baths
Bowls
Busts
Finials
Follies
Fountains
Obelisks
Pavilions
Pedestals
Pergolas
Plinths
Pool surrounds
Seats
Staddle stones
Statues
Sundials
Tables
Temples
Troughs
Urns
Vases

JURO ANTIQUES

Juro Antiques
Whitbourne
Worcester
WR6 5SF
01886 821 261
www.juro.co.uk
Open: Mon – Sat 9 – 5 (closed 1 – 2)
Sundays and evenings by appointment

The more divorced we become from the means of food production, which is now a vast global industry, the rosier a glow we cast over our rural past. With long hours, hard physical labour and huge uncertainties over livestock yields and crop harvests, farming was never an easy life, but it is a rich part of the UK's cultural heritage and today everybody wants a piece of it. There is an increasing advocacy of traditional land-management techniques, markets for organic small-holders are flourishing, and more gardeners are growing their own fruit and vegetables. Nevertheless, it is a simple fact that much of our farmland is disappearing fast under urban sprawl, and what does remain to us has to be tended with the very latest in modern technology to make it even remotely viable in economic terms.

Rather than letting old farming equipment rust into oblivion or disappear as landfill, why not give it a whole new lease of life on your own patch of ground? I'm not for a moment

PRODUCTS INCLUDE:
Benches
Blacksmiths' equipment
Carriages
Carts
Cartwheels
Cider mills
Cider presses
Farm machinery
Fountains
Millstones
Pumps
Staddle stones
Troughs

suggesting you plough up your lawn or winnow the seedheads of your decorative grasses, but I am suggesting you look afresh at the honest dignity of cattle troughs and cartwheels, water pumps and wheelbarrows when decorating your garden.

Roy Hughes and Judy George of Juro Antiques travel widely both here and on the continent to rescue agricultural antiques, buying direct from landowners, at specialist fairs and at farm auctions. Some items are even sourced from as far away as Poland and China.

Enormous circular cider mills with an upright crushing wheel once powered by man or beast take on a new lease of life as flower or herb planters, looking especially good in the turning circle of a large driveway, or in the yard of a barn conversion. Staddle stones, those giant mushrooms once used to raise granaries and storehouses off the ground to keep them free of rising damp and clambering vermin, are not only good to look at, they remind us of our roots.

Juro's excellent website is regularly updated to whet your appetite for a visit, and if you can't accommodate the larger items they offer, you'd be hard pushed not to find something of more appropriate size in their two-storey showroom of antique tools, garden ornaments and country furniture.

MARK PEDRO
DE LA TORRE

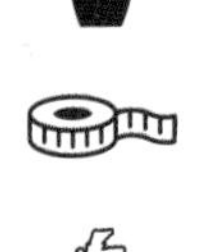

PRODUCTS INCLUDE:
Contemporary ceramics
Large outdoor vessels in spun steel, cast iron and aluminium

Mark Pedro de la Torre
The Courtyard
Old Rectory
Stoke Lacy
Herefordshire
HR7 4HH
01432 820 500
Viewing by appointment

It is a truth universally acknowledged that decorative cast-iron work reached its apogee in the Victorian era. The evidence is all around us. Original urns and benches are highly sought after and the designs are much reproduced to feed modern demand. Quite right too – you can't improve on perfection. But, alongside all this, wouldn't it be interesting to see cast iron through a fresh pair of eyes? To see it reappraised and reinvented as a new and challenging medium? To see it worked in a modern idiom? Look no further, then, than the work of Mark Pedro de la Torre.

While studying Three-Dimensional Design at Middlesex Polytechnic, Mark Pedro had a placement period as a finds assistant in the archaeology department of The Museum of London. While there, he wrote a dissertation on street ironmongery. Though his main field of endeavour was ceramics, this interlude amongst lampposts, pillar boxes and coal-hole covers was to have an unexpected influence later on in his career as an artist.

As a potter, much of Mark Pedro's work has taken the torus – a cylindrical ring – as its basic form. Thrown on a wheel from Staffordshire sanded red clay, his plump vessels are at once organic and industrial looking, reminiscent both of blood corpuscles and of hugely inflated tyres. All rim, and yet all bowl, turning ever towards their own centre, these creations have a fascinating dynamism while ineluctably focusing our attention on the plants at their core.

Finding that clay sometimes restricted the scale and scope of his work, an award from West Midlands Arts gave Mark Pedro the opportunity to work with a foundry to cast large pieces in iron. The results, weighty vessels a metre in diameter, whose form and rust-red surface pay homage to their pottery forebears, are astonishing. And I don't think it will be long at all before they're popping up in dissertations themselves.

Also ripe for a place in history, and representing a further collaboration between artist and industry, Mark has recently produced planters that have been spun from sheets of stainless steel. Satin-finished or mirror-polished, the effect in a garden is electric.

MICHAEL HILL

Michael Hill
Cressy Hall
Gosberton
Spalding
Lincolnshire
PE11 4JD
01775 840 925
Viewing by appointment

If you need proof of the strength and durability of cast iron, look no further than the Coalbrookdale Bridge. Designed by Thomas Pritchard and erected over the River Severn by John Wilkinson and Abraham Darby in 1777–79, partly as an advertisement for their famous foundry, it was in continual use by heavy traffic well into the 1950s and has now become a treasured national monument. From being a backbone of the eighteenth-century Industrial Revolution, by the early nineteenth century the Coalbrookdale Company had become a reputed world leader in artistic and decorative castings. Its garden furniture was taken very much to heart by the British, who not only used it at home but took it to the furthest outposts of the Empire. So admired were these intricate creations, they provided much inspiration to European and American manufacturers too, who went on to develop distinctive patterns of their own.

The Coalbrookdale Company and other giants like them no longer exist, and original pieces are highly sought-after antiques, but traditionally made reproductions are still to be had. Michael Hill's castings are of exceptional quality, and the range he offers is exquisite.

Michael has gone to extraordinary lengths to track down the most fashionable designs. The original for his Fern and Blackberry bench was bought from an old rag-and-bone man who was carting it away as scrap metal in 80 or so pieces. It had to be painstakingly reconstructed as a three-dimensional jigsaw puzzle before a cast could be made. One of the fountains was salvaged from a Maharajah's palace in India. Another even came from Australia.

'I've always found the designs strangely incompatible with other things of the period; they're ahead of their time really', he says. 'Just look at any of the benches – you'd never see anything so ornate in a chair for indoors.'

Confections of scrolls and trelliswork, intertwining vines and overlapping leaves, these benches have an instant affinity with any well-planted garden. Just like all the other items Michael offers they can be painted any colour you want in the Cressy Hall workshops to blend in or contrast with their surroundings.

CAST IRONWARE INCLUDES:
Archways
Benches
Chairs
Fountains
Gates
Gazebos
Love seats
Railings
Standpipes
Tables
Urns
Wall taps

PATIO PLANTING

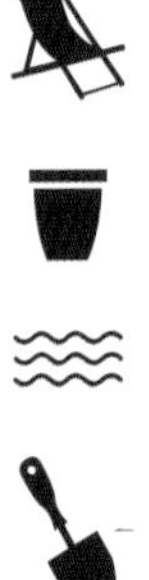

PRODUCTS INCLUDE:
Barometers & thermometers
Bird houses & feeders
Cards & gift wrap
Clothing & footwear
Filigree plant stands
Gardeners' soaps & unguents
Hand-painted weathervanes
Heavy glass vases
Lanterns & candles
Le Prince Jardinier tools & accessories
Trompe l'oeil features
Quality hand tools

Patio Planting
Cobb Hall Yard
St Paul's Lane
Lincoln
LN1 3AX
01522 536 573
Open: Mon – Sat 10 – 5

Gardeners are a happy and contented bunch, and Patio Planting's vivacious owner Hazel Hallam is a shining example of the breed. There's just no mistaking how much she adores her shop and customers – she positively bubbles over with enthusiasm. As Hazel explains: 'It's a joy to come to work when you're surrounded by everything you like in life.' That joy rubs off on her helpful and friendly staff too.

The people who flock to Patio Planting's door have already got, or have had in the past, the day-to-day products supplied by garden centres. They come here for goods which are that little bit different, and Hazel searches long and hard to keep them running back for more. Tourists visiting the stunning castle and cathedral, Lincolnshire shoppers homing in on their county town, and Lincoln locals simply taking the air clearly love her taste and style. Nothing stays on the shelves for long, and each time you visit there'll be something different to please the eye and to tempt your purse. At pocket-money prices you'll find Hazel's trademark green ceramic wellies – which she knows full well that people ultimately use as pen and pencil holders but which she often plants up first with herbs or scented narcissi as ready-made gifts. As for the rest... You might find oriental garden parasols; clocks, barometers and thermometers; superior planters in wood, terracotta and lead; clean-lined metal obelisks and stylish, self-contained water features. Then again, there are twirly-stemmed bay trees, topiarized box, willow sculptures trained up with ivy, and luxuriant potted tree ferns at prices to die for. And that's not to mention the tools, cushions and footwear from the le Prince Jardinier range, nor the decorative stonework and bleached-out coffee wood garden furniture.

A little place with a big personality, Patio Planting's stock spills out into the surrounding courtyard of speciality shops, embracing it with ornament and greenery. The girl can't help herself: not only did Hazel spend years with top developers creating gardens for luxury homes but she also once ran a smallholding supplying organic produce to the restaurant trade and she still designs gardens on a consultancy basis for private clients. Horticulture is in her bones. A simple fact you'll realize when you visit.

RAFFLES THATCHED GARDEN BUILDINGS

Raffles Thatched Garden Buildings
Church Farm
Main Street
Overseal
Derbyshire
DE12 6LG
01283 762 469
www.rafflesgb.com
Site visits by arrangement

Brothers Andrew and David Raffle are both time-served master thatchers who specialize in recreating rustic garden pavilions from original Victorian and Edwardian designs. Far more than picturesque follies, their summer-houses provide shelter from the wind, they are excellent places for entertaining (and canoodling), they can be sited for sun or shade, and discreet storage space for tools, mowers and sports equipment can be built into them.

The buildings are constructed in timber and other traditional materials, and can be decorated externally and internally in a variety of ways. They can be stained, painted, varnished or clad with bark in intricate patterns. Interior walls can also be lined with heather, moss or pinecones. Gnarled old branches can be criss-crossed into ornate tracery window frames. Floors can be of stone, brick, concrete, pebble mosaic or of rounds sawn from logs. An unusual, not to say grisly, restoration project even involved relaying a worn old floor with around 16,000 sheep's knuckle-bones – Greek symbols of divinity. The end result was a triumph of purity and simplicity which rather belies all the labour involved in sourcing, cleaning and finally setting the bones into position. Looking back, David says it was 'like stuffing a mattress with wrens' feathers' – it certainly demonstrates the brothers' grit, determination and attention to detail.

After an initial visit and consultation, much of the construction can be done in the Raffles' own workshop before each structure is ready to be assembled on site and given its final crowning glory of thatch. The Raffles occasionally use Norfolk reed where a formal look is required as very precise patterns can be dressed into it, but straw is the material of choice to complement most of their rustic work. Where a very rugged appearance is called for, say in a woodland, then heather is brought into play. They once even re-thatched a centuries-old building in gorse. Ouch.

SERVICES INCLUDE:
Design, construction & restoration of rustic summer-houses

SCOTTS OF THRAPSTON

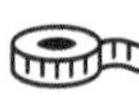

PRODUCTS INCLUDE:
Field shelters
Gazebos
Pavilions
Revolving summer-houses
Spas
Stables

Scotts of Thrapston
Bridge Street
Thrapston
Northamptonshire
NN14 4LR
01832 732 366
www.scottsofthrapston.co.uk
Phone for sales and viewing details

Established in 1920 by James Scott, and still a family business to this day, Scotts of Thrapston is a large specialist joinery company and one of the country's leading suppliers of stables, poolside pavilions and luxury summer-houses.

Equestrian buildings can be made to any size and specification, and sympathetic local materials will be used wherever possible. You can have anything from a simple and straightforward field shelter for a family pony to a professional yard with a whole series of stables, haystores and workshops. Scotts also constructs garages and storerooms to blend in with existing architecture, so utilitarian garden structures need never be a blot on your landscape.

For a spot of unashamed indulgence in even the smallest of gardens, Scotts produces tailor-made summer-houses too. Each stylish octagonal structure is glazed for warmth by day, comes with shutters to ensure privacy by night, and the removable door panels mean it can be opened up for plenty of fresh air whenever the weather suits. It can be painted in any colour with a choice of upholstery for the integral seating, and an optional lounger insert for creating a big double bed. The roof can be made of slate-effect glass fibre, it can be clad in natural cedar shingles, or it can also be given a hand-folded copper covering. To get the sunshine or starlight shining in from above there's also a part-glazed option on the slate-effect roof. Most ingenious of all, a rotating base mechanism can be fitted: popularized by the Victorians, this lets you change your view of the garden whenever you wish and also means that you can follow the sun throughout the course of the day.

For the ultimate in outdoor decadence, though, you just have to see Scotts' garden hot tubs. The intimate Hot Hut opens to reveal a heated whirlpool bath complete with adjustable hydrotherapy jets. The larger Garden Spa provides a seating and changing area too. They're the perfect evening retreat for ladies of leisure and for gardeners wanting to relieve aching muscles.

STEPHEN MCRAE

Stephen McRae
Wood House
Staplow
Ledbury
Herefordshire
HR8 1NP
01531 640 051
Viewing by appointment

Truly exciting and innovative metalwork is rare, so Stephen McRae is an artist and craftsman to be cherished. Using steel, wrought iron, copper and brass, he forges gates, fountains, and sculptures of trees and flowers, the likes of which you've never seen before.

Palm-tree fountains soaring five metres tall like 'Trachycarpus Galvanisus' and 'Trachycarpus Silvarium'; styled poppy seed pots releasing ionised mist that trickles down their ribbed sides; boundaries and screens like the extraordinarily realistic 'Fig Tree' gate with its secret opening – these are just some of the many creations to spring from his ever-fertile imagination.

Apart from the natural movement and growth that metals allow for when hot, they can subsequently be coloured and patinated in an almost limitless palette. Plant forms therefore lend themselves perfectly to Stephen's art. Past commissions have included a stainless-steel 'Tree' sprinkler for a golf course in Spain, a water sculpture in the foyer of an international pharmaceuticals giant in London and even an entire town garden made of metal for a wealthy private client.

Before attending Hereford College of Art and Design for an HND course in Design Craft, Stephen completed a degree in Architecture at the South Bank University. This may well account for the importance of negative as well as positive space in his work. In his abstract 'companion' water sculptures, interlocking shapes roll over each other to form channels and gullies but they also capture and frame surrounding views. His 'One to Another' pieces, largely derived from leaf shapes, merge into the surrounding air via a dynamic network of tendrils.

All pieces are made to order, and Stephen will make site visits where clients want something specifically relevant to their gardens. Who knows what gems might emerge next?

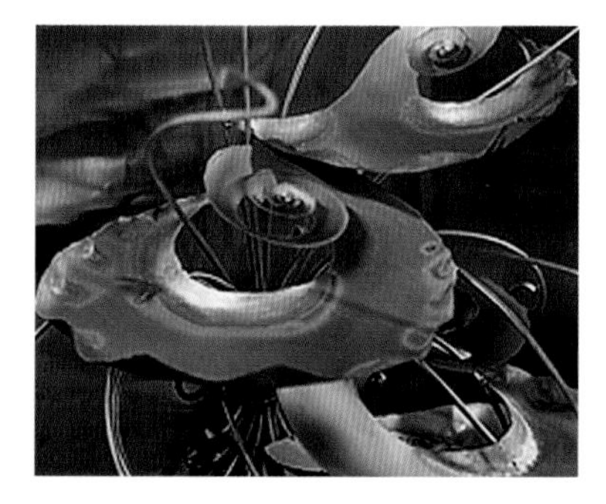

PRODUCTS:
Exquisite metalwork
& sculpture based
on natural forms

WHICHFORD
POTTERY

PRODUCTS INCLUDE:
- Ali Baba pots
- Basket pots
- 'Eclipse' pots
- Edging tiles
- Elephant planters
- Floor tiles
- Half pots
- Herb pots
- Kale & rhubarb forcers
- Long toms
- Orange pots
- Oval pots
- Saucers
- Tableware
- Wall masks

Whichford Pottery
Whichford
Nr Shipston-on-Stour
Warwickshire
CV36 5PG
01608 684 416
www.whichfordpottery.com
Open: Mon – Fri 9 – 5
Sat 10 – 4
Occasionally Sun

Not counting the glorious scenery it nestles into, the Whichford Pottery has three enormous draws. On weekdays you can watch pots being made by hand. In the gardens and yards you can see how beautifully pots can be planted up and then grouped together into stunning floral displays. Fired with enthusiasm to take something of this glory back home with you, there is then the option to buy anything you like from Whichford's extraordinary range – at the last count they had about 250 different lines.

Founded by Jim Keeling in 1976, the pottery has a worldwide reputation for excellence both in terms of design and in the quality of materials and manufacture. Through its extravagant exhibits at the Chelsea Flower Show each year, Whichford adds ever more fans to its loyal band of followers.

The vast majority of the pots are thrown by hand and then decorated on the wheel using patterned rollers and finger and thumb 'pastry-work'. Others are left to stiffen for a day or two before being embossed with flower or leaf motifs, or perhaps having extruded-clay strips woven around them in imitation of basketwork. Some pots are so large that they have to be thrown in separate sections which are then fused together. So ornate are others that they can only be made by pressing and beating the clay into plaster moulds.

Whatever the size or shape of a pot, however simply or elaborately it is decorated, nothing leaves Whichford without a date stamp and a ten-year guarantee against damage by frost. Because of this, no chances are taken with bought-in, ready-processed clay. Instead, the pottery prepares its own special mix on site. Three different types of freshly dug local clay are blended together to form a water 'slip' which is sieved, strained and then pressed into blocks which are left to mature before use.

With all this work going on and with such an enormous output, you might expect to find something of a factory set-up here. Not a bit of it. Harking back to an earlier time in our history, what the pottery has grown into over the years is an idyllic little self-contained hamlet with a staff of dedicated artisans. The magic of the place, and the magic in their hands, most assuredly rubs off on every one of the Whichford wares.

One-stop shopping in the form of quality independent garden centres, each with a special twist, is a welcome feature both in Northern Ireland and in the north of England. The Landscape Centre in Dunadry offers a stimulating design forum; staff knowledge and customer service at Donaghadee are exemplary; at Plants of Special Interest in Braithwell the evocation of the Mediterranean is, quite frankly, astonishing.

One of the fascinating things to emerge here is a lofty disregard among serious gardeners for modern implements. The consensus is that they bend and break too easily, and that blades won't take a decent sharpening. Everyone seems to have a kit of tools of utterly indeterminate age but with a measurable amount of clout. They are passed down in families, they are handed over the garden wall to newly-weds by elderly neighbours, and they are stocked at discerning shops and salvage yards.

If Northerners make something, they make it well and they make it to last. The Iron Design Company's furniture is built for wear as well as for looks. Pennine Playgrounds make the sturdiest children's play equipment I've ever seen, and Maggy Howarth's cobblestone designs will outlive a good many generations to come.

NORTH OF ENGLAND AND NORTHERN IRELAND

ANDY THORNTON

Andy Thornton
Victoria Mills
Stainland Road
Greetland
Halifax
West Yorkshire
HX4 8AD
01422 377 314
www.ataa.co.uk
Open: Mon – Fri 8.30 – 5.30
Sat 9 – 5

It is easy to get carried away with excitement at Andy Thornton's. It is possible you'll be a little bit bewildered and bedazzled. It is also quite likely that you'll get lost, so be sure to hang on to your nearest and dearest. There are more than 6,000 square metres of display space in this vast, many-storeyed former cotton mill, and there's an awful lot going on here, so perhaps a little background would be helpful.

After training in Art and Design, Andy spent four years working and backpacking his way round the world. In the States, he came across and became involved in the huge auctions supplying a nostalgia-crazed hospitality industry with British and European architectural salvage. On his return to the UK, Andy started sourcing and consigning stock to these auctions in his own right. At the same time he realized there was huge potential in the home market for the redevelopment of pubs, restaurants and hotels caught in the vinyl-cushioned and Formica table-topped doldrums. What brasseries and leisure chains in this country wanted, though, wasn't just a ready source of panelling, ironwork and country antiques; they wanted a complete design-and-installation service for both indoors and out. Andy rose to the challenge and business rocketed. To complement original fixtures and fittings, Andy had to begin making reproduction pieces to keep up with demand, and this now means that Victoria Mills can fulfil almost any dreams you have for decorative items, ancient or modern, for your home or your garden.

If you want a row of 'gas' lamps either side of your driveway and beautiful cast-iron railings along the street, Andy Thornton can oblige. If you want an ornate gazebo with a glass roof, you can have that too. But you might just want a Mediterranean oil jar or two, a small stone trough, an original pump to turn into a water feature or a ready-made wall-mounted fountain. Or a cartwheel or two. A milk churn. A wheelbarrow. A bench, or a table and chairs. I promise, you'll be spoilt for choice.

PRODUCTS INCLUDE:

Benches & seats
Bird-baths
Cartwheels
Fountains
Gates
Lampposts
Milk churns
Oil jars
Pavilions
Plinths
Pots & planters
Pumps
Railings
Statuary in bronze,
lead & stone
Sundials
Troughs
Wall masks
Wall-mounted water
Features
Wheclbarrows
Wind vanes

DONAGHADEE
GARDEN CENTRE

PRODUCTS INCLUDE:
Alexander Rose garden furniture
Barbecues
Benches
Gardening gifts
Patio heaters
Plant supports
Secateurs
Self-contained water features
Shears
Statuary
Terracotta pots
Trellising
Wind chimes

Donaghadee Garden Centre
34 Stockbridge Road
Donaghadee
County Down
BT21 0PN
028 9188 3603
Open: Mon – Sat 9.30 – 5.30
Thu 9.30 – 8.00
Sun 12.30 – 5.30

Good vibrations count for a lot. There's a buzz and a friendliness about the Donaghadee Garden Centre which makes you realize straight away that it is an independently run concern and not part of a large and impersonal chain. Director John Richardson says: 'We work very, very hard at creating a pleasant atmosphere for people to come into, and we're relentless about providing a high level of customer service.' That work certainly pays off.

An obvious draw is the busy and welcoming coffee shop which serves freshly prepared seasonal food that is cooked on the premises. Something you notice straightaway at Donaghadee is that new arrivals pulling up in their cars will make an immediate bee-line for the place. This is the absolute reverse of the usual garden-centre phenomenon where refreshments are very much an afterthought of the management and even for tired and hungry shoppers, only seen as a last resort.

Indoors and out, Donaghadee aims to create a beautiful garden atmosphere all year round and you'll always find an inspiring range of plants for both home and garden in the peak of condition. Success breeds success here – quality is high, turnover is rapid, and you know that each time you visit there'll be something new to look out for. The well-trained and approachable staff are always happy to advise on growing requirements, and you may well find that they remember what you bought on your last visit and ask how it settled in.

If you're as interested in outdoor entertaining and decoration as in gardening *per se*, there's a good selection of Alexander Rose garden furniture including picnic tables and parasols; there are patio heaters, attractive but sensibly priced statuary, and some interesting and unusual terracotta pots. There are tools and sundries in abundance and garden-related gifts in the form of lotions and potions and decorative homewares. Your gardening wants satisfied, you'll leave happy in body and soul.

ERRINGTON REAY & CO.

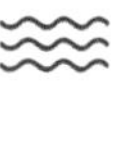

PRODUCTS INCLUDE:
- Alpine bowls
- Cylinder pots
- Herb pots
- Jugs
- Rhubarb forcers
- Rope-twist edging
- Saucers
- Strawberry pots
- Trumpet pots

Errington Reay & Co Ltd
Bardon Mill
Hexham
Northumberland
NE47 7HU
01434 344 245
www.erringtonreay.co.uk
Open: daily 9–5

This is a place rich in industrial history. The works are in a former water-powered woollen mill which began operating in the seventeenth century and gave the entire village its name. When Messrs. Errington and Reay established their pottery in 1878, salt-glazed stoneware was in great demand and a large site was essential if the business was to thrive. Although this was the era of plant-hunting throughout the British Empire and beyond, the cry was not for flower pots by the ton, but rather for chimney-pots and for strong, durable and non-porous sanitary ware – the gullies, bricks, the drainage pipes and the unmentionables so necessary to towns and cities throughout the building heyday of the late nineteenth century.

Storage jars, ornamental pottery for domestic use and the decorative rope- or barley-twist edging for pathways and flower borders characteristic of Victorian villa gardens were always strong sidelines, and as the decades rolled by, so the emphasis in production changed. Today, Errington Reay focuses on producing a quality range of frost-proof gardenware that it sells through selected outlets across the UK, at garden shows, and direct to the public from its shop at Bardon Mill.

All the pots are hand-thrown by the local workforce – many of whose families have worked here for generations – and are then fired in either of two vast, mausoleum-like kilns. Atmospheric pressure and external temperature can affect their performance, so controlling these brutes remains very much an art passed from father to son. At a critical stage in the process, salt is injected, which vaporises into gas under the intense heat and coats the pots with a deliciously attractive treacle-brown glaze. The unpredictability of all this means that 10–15 per cent of a firing will be classified as seconds under the company's rigorous quality-control system and this is where the factory shop comes into its own. People travel from far and wide, even hiring vans and taking orders from friends, to buy pots at truly bargain prices which can barely be distinguished from the perfect article. As far as I'm concerned, a surface mark or a blemish here or there simply adds to the charm of the pieces. As a further inducement, other on-site goodies include life-size slip-cast hens, cats and shells rarely offered for sale elsewhere.

If I've whetted your appetite but you're not up to the journey, Errington Reay offers free delivery on mail-order, telephone or internet orders above certain value, so you can enjoy the products without paying for the post.

HAVENPLAN

PRODUCTS INCLUDE:

- Anchors
- Animal feeders
- Chimney-pots
- Decorative ironwork
- Fireplaces
- Gates
- Millstones
- Mines
- Ornamental masonry
- Shop signs
- Stone troughs
- Street lamps
- Telephone boxes
- Village pumps
- Weathervanes

Havenplan
The Old Station
Station Road
Killamarsh
Sheffield
Yorkshire
S21 8EN
0114 248 9972
Open: Tue, Wed, Thu, Sat 10 – 2.30

The biggest, most coveted piece of architectural heritage here is not, alas, for sale. But you can forgive the Buckle family for hanging on to it. It's the building they run their business from.

Havenplan, just a whistle-stop away from Derbyshire's ruggedly beautiful Peak District, is housed in a Victorian railway station which once had around 30 steam trains a day hurtling through. Engine buffs might like to know that Mallard and the Flying Scotsman were regular visitors. Today's arrivals and departures though, are on an altogether different track, consisting of gardeners and home-makers fired with a passion for unusual decorative items from the past.

It all began in the modernising 1970s with the chance purchase by John Buckle and his wife Margaret of a consignment of pews from a local church. Old gas and electric street lamps soon followed. Telephone boxes became available by the lorryload, cast-iron gates and railings from factories under demolition were saved from melting down. The stock just grew and grew. Daughter Melanie Robinson regularly scours the country to keep it all topped up, so the joy of each visit is that you never know what bygones you might find – or what use they might be put to.

Chimney-pots of all shapes and sizes are always popular for growing plants in, but so too are the old salt-glazed stoneware toilets of the kind once made by Errington Reay of Bardon Mill. Stone troughs and sturdy metal cattle feeders make excellent planters too, but they can also be used as simple garden ponds. Rustic millstones or elaborately carved blocks from city-centre buildings are perfect ornaments in themselves, but with a pump, a sump and a little ingenuity buyers can easily turn them into handsome water features. An anchor from a Whitby whaling vessel or a mine fished out of Plymouth Harbour would be quite a conversation piece, and a weathervane will always turn heads. And if you've ever wondered what people do with old phone boxes once they get them home, Melanie tells me that one client turned his into an aquarium, while another one was made into a poolside shower! Most imaginative of all, a recent customer bought a fine old fireplace to install against a garden wall ready for planting up with flame-coloured flowers and foliage.

THE IRON
DESIGN COMPANY

PRODUCTS INCLUDE:
Deckchairs
Dining tables & chairs
Garden benches
Rocking chairs
Side tables
Sun loungers

The Iron Design Company
8 Royal Parade
Harrogate
North Yorkshire
HG1 2SZ
01423 538 725
www.irondesign.co.uk
Open: Tue – Fri 10 – 5
Sat 10 – 4

1 Verulam Road
St Albans
Hertfordshire
AL3 4DA
Open: Tue – Fri 10 – 5
Sat 10 – 4

Graham Todd of the Iron Design Company has a steel industry background so knows more than a thing or two about quality metalwork. Substantial frames and supremely strong joints ensure that every item of furniture can take life's hard knocks and certainly won't give under pressure. You can really lounge on the loungers and you can sit back as firmly as you like in the chairs. This is nothing like the mass-produced stuff you gingerly lower yourself into. While lightweight rusted metal pergolas and plant supports can be cheap and beautiful additions to the garden, metal furniture that rusts is neither use nor ornament and always a false economy. All of the Iron Design Company's outdoor pieces are galvanized by being dipped in molten zinc before a chip-resistant paint is applied. They are delivered to your door with a 15-year warranty against corrosion, which means that what look like elegant dining room or conservatory suites are in fact built to stand up to permanent outdoor use.

In the same way that the Dedon line of furniture supplied by Leisure Plan in the south-east of England makes you do a double-take when you see it in the garden, so the range on offer here really helps you to break down the visual boundaries between indoor and outdoor living. The two- and three-seater French-influenced benches are obvious outdoor pieces, but who'd have thought of a rocking chair for the lawn?

There are 40 or so paint colours to choose from; removable seat cushions come in a wide selection of showerproof fabrics; and tables can be topped with natural granite in all sorts of shades and patterns. As to the furniture designs themselves, the variety is infinite.

There are many standard ranges on display, but because everything is made to order, all tables and chairs can be altered in size or design to accommodate any individual requirements you might have. If you simply can't wait the six weeks it takes to fulfil your dreams, you are of course welcome to purchase showroom stock on the spot. Besides the main Harrogate shop there's also a branch in St Albans, and the company has a mail-order catalogue too.

JENNI WALKER'S
POTTING SHED

Jenni Walker's Potting Shed
6 Montpellier Mews
Harrogate
North Yorkshire
HG1 2TQ
01423 526 988
Open: Mon – Fri 9–5
Sat 9–5.30

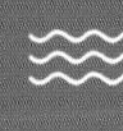

PRODUCTS INCLUDE:
Antique tools
Benches
Bird-baths
Bird houses
Bulbs
Candles
Chairs & tables
Cut flowers
Garden sprays
Lanterns
Lead statuary
Plants
Pots & planters
Rustic arches
Trugs
Statuary
Urns
Wall planters
Wirework
Wrought-iron gates

In a labyrinthine warren of buildings and stone walkways once belonging to the Crown, Jenni Walker opened her Potting Shed after 'retiring' from a successful career in floristry. Montpellier Mews, as the name suggests, was once a stables complex, but in Harrogate's Victorian heyday as one of Europe's largest spa towns, its primary function was as a store for the hundreds upon hundreds of bath chairs used for ferrying sick and valetudinarian visitors from their luxury hotels to the Pump Rooms. Nowadays the Montpellier Quarter is alive with restaurants, antique shops and bars, the most renowned of which – and backing directly on to Jenni's shop – is The Drum and Monkey, as well regarded by younger tourists and locals as Betty's Tea Rooms are by an older generation.

Originally occupying just the tiniest of sites, Jenni's business grew and grew in terms of turnover and eventually knocked through into premises next door, making it the strangely shaped, beautifully arranged, indoor and outdoor experience you see today.

Jenni's husband Martin takes monthly trips to northern France to bring back antique wirework tables and chairs, wrought-iron gates, garden statues and any other treasures he might alight on. Jenni tracks down antique garden tools and ornaments in the UK, as well as buying in a selection of modern pieces and cut flowers, bulbs (which she pots up beautifully), and living plants such as bay trees, lavender, rosemary and marguerites to soften the look.

Besides a dedicated band of Harrogate locals, Jenni has regular customers from all over the north of England who travel especially to rifle through her stock. One customer buys only antique garden sprays, another collects just secateurs. Many come at Christmas-time to collect the specially ordered wreaths, garlands and swags Jenni still makes by hand to deck their doors, halls and fireplaces. Throughout the year, Jenni benefits from dedicated garden visitors from the nearby RHS grounds at Harlow Carr, and once in Harrogate they are often surprised at the opulence of the town's own Valley Gardens and Montpellier Gardens. They might walk away with a Victorian child's wheelbarrow with miniature tools, an Edwardian lady's rose cutter for snipping and then holding on to high-up blooms, or a fine piece of new or antique lead statuary. And if, as is the want of sightseers they leave only with happy memories, it will be a long time before they see so lovely a shop as Jenni's.

THE LANDSCAPE CENTRE

PRODUCTS INCLUDE:
Arbours
Bamboo deer-scarers
Bird-baths
Bird feeders
Cast-stone ornaments
Dovecotes
Garden furniture
Gardening gifts
Hanging baskets
Houseplants
Koi carp & other fish
Metal & terracotta planters
Mirrored balls
Parasols
Plant supports
Plants, shrubs & trees
Volcanic stone carvings
Wall masks

The Landscape Centre
24 Donegore Hill
Dunadry
Antrim
BT41 2QU
028 9443 2175
www.landscapecentre.net
Open: Mon–Sat 9–6
Sun 1–6

Just a couple of miles from Templepatrick and within an area of outstanding natural beauty, the picturesque hamlet of Donegore in County Antrim has been a focus of mankind for at least five millennia. Although archaeologists have uncovered traces of an extensive Stone Age settlement dating back to 3,000 BC, the most visible evidence of early human activity here has got to be the motte. Pronounced 'moat' hereabouts, this is a dumpy artificial hill beside the Belfast to Antrim road that was built as a military look-out by the Anglo-Normans. The name Donegore, though, comes from Dún Ó g Corra meaning 'fort of the Corrs' and this suggests that an Irish fort preceded the Norman earthworks. Be all that as it may, the stronghold of civilization here is undoubtedly to be found on the natural hillsides rising up majestically behind. Where the United Irishmen gathered in 1798, the Landscape Centre run by John and Kaye Campbell now firmly holds its ground.

The business began in 1980 as a plant wholesalers, but spurred on by John's master's degree in Landscape Architecture it soon became not only a retail plant centre but a design studio too, offering a complete planning and construction service. The company today is one of Ireland's leading landscapers, with a crack in-house team.

The enthusiasm for plants and for garden design here is infectious. There is an outdoor Design Forum of ten different garden vignettes showing how plants, ornaments and landscaping materials can be combined in a variety of styles. An area or two is redesigned every few months, so there's something new to see each time you visit.

The Landscape Centre has more than 20 working water features on display, including tipping bamboo deer-scarers and gleaming futuristic mirrored balls. There's a wide selection of unusual terracotta for sale, and some quality garden furniture too, both in traditional teak and in sleek metal mesh. Ornaments include fine cast-stone work for a classical look, and – particular favourites with Kaye – an intriguing range of modernist sculptures hand-carved in Java from volcanic rock.

MAGGY HOWARTH
COBBLESTONE DESIGNS

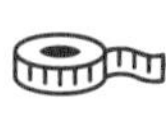

PRODUCTS:
Pebble mosaics

Maggy Howarth
Cobblestone Designs
Hilltop
Wennington
Lancaster
LA2 8NY
01524 274 264
www.maggyhowarth.co.uk
Works to commission

After a fine-art training as a painter, Maggy Howarth was involved for many years in performance art and experimental theatre as both sculptor and player, travelling all around the UK as well as abroad. In solid contrast to the ephemeral, fleeting nature of events and happenings, Maggy's subsequent career as a pebble mosaicist, the pebble mosaicist, has laid down a body of work with incredible substance and permanence. Yet there is a connection between her two fields of endeavour.

On returning to her Lancashire farmhouse between tours, practised at responding to environments, places and atmosphere and accustomed to working with whatever materials came readily to hand, Maggy found inspiration in the traditional cobblery of surrounding villages and began experimenting in her own garden using locally gathered pebbles. And because she is an artist, that cobbling soon turned into something quite extraordinary.

From working outside directly on the ground, embedding stones of different sizes, shapes and colours in a dry bedding mix of sand and cement, Maggy developed a pre-casting technique that gives her greater artistic freedom and that allows her, where necessary, to achieve incredibly fine detail with pebbles far smaller than normal.
Each mosaic is formed upside down in a series of moulds in the shelter of Maggy's studio, then the various segments are assembled on site in the manner of a giant jigsaw puzzle before being seamlessly grouted together. The practical advantages are that Maggy and her team can work all year round whatever the weather, for clients installation is quick and, from the perspective of pedestrians, it is worth pointing out that the finished surface is comfortably level underfoot.

Be it a mythological scene, a study from nature of a swirling geometric pattern, the design of each piece arises both out of a dialogue between Maggy and her clients, and from a sense of what is naturally appropriate to the site. The end results are like paintings in stone, with the flow of pebbles like brushstrokes from a master's hand.

If you would like to learn more about this fascinating subject, Maggy is the author of two books: *The Art of Pebble Mosaics* and *The Complete Book of Pebble Mosaics*.

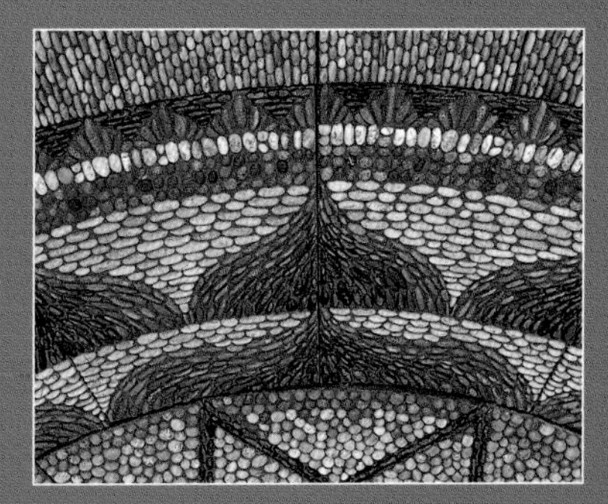

OVER THE GARDEN WALL

Over the Garden Wall
93 Commercial Street
Norton
Malton
North Yorkshire
YO17 9HY
01653 698 880
www.overthegardenwall.com
Open: Tue, Wed, Fri, Sat 10 – 5
Ring to check times Tue – Wed
Also open by appointment

PRODUCTS INCLUDE:
Asparagus trugs
Bottle racks
Bulb pans
Cast-iron animals
Cast-iron posts
Cucumber trugs
Edging tiles
Florists' vases & buckets
Garden furniture
Garden signs
Kale & rhubarb forcers
Land drains
Market garden trugs
Olive-oil jars
Plant labels
Plant stands
Sap pots
Seed boxes
Show vases
Soft fruit baskets
Stacking trugs
Statuary
Terracotta pots & saucers
Tools of all kinds
Urns
Wheelbarrows

Quite irrespective of their quality, whether we buy them at DIY sheds and garden centres or from department stores and the most recherché of garden shops, today's garden tools are all general-purpose off-the-peg numbers. Many tools of yesteryear however – more than you'd ever imagine – were made individually by a blacksmith with a very specific purpose and often with a particular person in mind. They've therefore got a tale to tell. Stewart Pote, owner of Over the Garden Wall, is a connoisseur, enthusiast and man-in-the-know who can read them all like books.

The thicker the tread of the spade – the part of its blade where you put your foot – the heavier the soil. The narrower the blade, the heavier still. Clay spades even had hollow mid-sections, so sticky was the earth, so resistant to friction. The thicker the shaft, the stronger the labourer and the heavier the land; the longer the shaft, the taller the man. Long- and straight-shafted spades give the best options for leverage and help lofty gardeners like myself keep their backs straight while digging. Simple 'T' grips are easier to push down on, though, and suit people with large hands, while cut-out 'O' handles mounted on the top of a shaft and more expensive 'wishbone' handles – made by splitting the shaft and them steaming it apart before inserting a hand-grip – not only allow for pressure but make twisting actions easier. Shovels, of course, with their curving sides, allow for carrying things too. And let's not even get on to forks (although blunt-ended ones are generally for harvesting root vegetables like beets or potatoes, iand narrow tines are for aerating the soil, while splayed prongs are for lifting lightweight loads like manure or straw).

If you can match your own precise requirements with those of some gardener of an earlier generation you're lucky indeed. And if you want to take a shot, then Over the Garden Wall is the place to try.

It's also the shop for such fascinating bygones as market garden trugs and florists' vases, and for sensibly priced ornaments that don't break the bank. If you're mad about gardening but careful about what you spend then I'd strongly advise you to leap Over the Garden Wall.

PENNINE PLAYGROUNDS

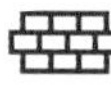

PRODUCTS INCLUDE:
- Climbers
- Cradle & toddler seats
- Fencing
- Fitness trails
- Goalposts
- Integrated play systems
- Monkey bars
- Picnic tables
- Planters
- Playground bark
- Recycled rubber surfacing
- Sandpits
- Seating
- Seesaws
- Slides
- Swings
- Trampolines
- Trapezes

Pennine Playgrounds
Waterside Business Park
Keighley Road
Silsden
West Yorkshire
BD20 0EA
01535 656 500
www.pennine-playgrounds.co.uk
Open: Mon – Fri 9 – 5

Mens sana in corpore sano, or healthy body, healthy mind. As parents themselves, Graham and Vicki Braithwaite of Pennine Playgrounds fully appreciate the value of active outdoor play in keeping children physically healthy and mentally alert. Their company was established in 1990 to offer design-and-build schemes catering to all budgets and specifications. Besides a multitude of private customers, they have the approval of parish and district councils, housing developers, landscape architects and they have more than 200 satisfied schools on their books.

Doctors and paediatricians might have all sorts of explanations as to why stimulation of the body and the senses, and spontaneous social interaction are so supremely beneficial, but common sense tells us all that a well-exercised and happily exhausted child with plenty of friends is bound to make greater progress in life than an early pallid victim of our insular television- and computer-obsessed age.

Safe and sturdy in rounded timber, Pennine Playgrounds' own two-seater Beamsley and one-seater Nesfield swing units are designed to be concreted into the ground and will give years of service. There's a range of interchangeable accessories, so that as children grow they can progress from either a traditional cradle seat or toddler seat to a flat seat, a belt seat and even a trapeze. The Hetton activity unit has two swings, a slide and a rope ladder, and the Askwith is an exciting climbing frame with ladders, monkey bars, a cargo net and a swinging tyre.

In addition to a commercial playground range made in Wales, the Braithwaites carry playstations from Belgium which can include slides, fireman's poles, clubhouses and climbing walls, and there are stand-alone items such as goalposts, sandpits and seesaws on giant springs. And some fabulous trampolines.

At the purpose-built showroom right by the Leeds and Liverpool Canal, staff are happy to advise on all your requirements and, as part of the comprehensive installation service, the company can also lay colourful, impact-absorbing surfaces made from recycled tyres – so lots of fun and no hard knocks.

PLANTS OF SPECIAL INTEREST

Plants of Special Interest
4 High Street
Braithwell
Nr Rotherham
South Yorkshire
S66 7AL
01709 790 642
www.psinursery.co.uk
Open: Tue – Sun 10 – 5

It's not only the plants here that are of special interest. It's everything.

The Dunstans have been farming their land in Braithwell for generations, but in the early 1990s Peter and Rita Dunstan and their son Jamie realized that diversification was essential if the family were to continue in business. A farm shop was slowly developed; Peter began growing sunflowers and pumpkins instead of traditional local crops; Rita began selling home-reared garden plants; Jamie branched out into landscaping. Word soon got about that something exciting was happening here. What you see today is a result not only of a great deal of hard work, but of the family paying careful attention to their customers' needs and then responding accordingly.

Even though people came from as far afield as America on account of the pumpkins, they never caught on commercially and were eventually dropped. The flourishing farm shop finally succumbed to supermarket competition. The gardening side of things, though, just grew and grew. More and more land was given over to raising plants. The nursery was soon listed in the *Plantfinder*. Peter and Rita's private garden has opened for the National Gardens Scheme. The old tannery was converted into a tea-room so that Rita could have somewhere to hold talks and demonstrations.

Now, that tea-room is a fully fledged restaurant. Besides unusual perennials, the nursery specializes in towering great cypresses, centuries-old olive trees, tree ferns and hardy palms. The grounds display smart summer-houses and other structures for sale. Outbuildings are packed with gorgeous gardening bygones such as wirework plant stands and antique iron urns. There are well-chosen contemporary items too. And unique stone carvings. And … And … As Rita says of the business: 'It has grown and gone off in all sorts of directions we could never have imagined; it's not something that could have happened overnight.'

There's a complete, fully rounded look on offer here: it's smart, it's Mediterranean, it's natural, it's quietly understated. It's perfect.

PRODUCTS INCLUDE:
Antique benches
Arbours
Architectural & unusual plants
Baskets
Candles
Cast-iron urns
Gazebos
Mature trees
Moroccan lanterns
Paving
Perennials, trees, ferns & palms
Staddle stones
Stationery
Stone carvings
Summer-houses
Terracotta pots & planters
Victorian cloches
Wickerwork
Wirework

THE POTTING SHED

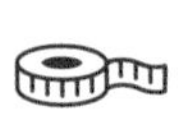

PRODUCTS INCLUDE:

Antiques
Aprons
Baskets
Bird houses
Books
Bulbs
Candles
Doors
Furniture
Glassware
Gloves
Labels
Mirrors
Obelisks
Potted bulbs
Pots & planters
Shutters
Stone obelisks & sphinxes
Tools
Trelliswork
Watering cans
Wheelbarrows

The Potting Shed
13 London Road
Alderley Edge
Cheshire
SK9 7JT
01625 585 819
Open: Mon – Fri 10 – 6
Sat 9.30 – 6
In Dec Sun 11 – 4

Alderley Edge lies a little to the south of Manchester amongst the rolling green pastures of Cheshire. In a picturesque setting, and with a handsome tree-lined Victorian high street, it takes its name from the nearby sandstone escarpment that rises so dramatically from the plain. Not only is this an excellent base from which to explore the gardens at Capesthorne Hall, Hare Hill and Little Moreton Hall – the most outstanding timber-framed moated house in Britain – and of course the arboretum at Jodrell Bank Observatory, Alderley Edge is also one of the nicest villages in the county for quality shopping.

After spending thirty years in the world of textiles and fashion, Norma Dawson wanted a change of direction. A keen amateur gardener with a professionally trained eye, she felt strongly that the north west deserved an alternative to the conventional garden centre, somewhere for discerning customers to buy things that were really special. So in 1997, The Potting Shed opened its doors for business.

In visual terms everything that goes on inside reflects the fact that gardening revolves around the seasons: the window displays are entirely re-themed four times a year, and the gift-wrapping subtly changes hue and tone as the months pass by. As part of the service, no purchase, however large or small, from an antique wheelbarrow to a tiny terracotta heart, leaves the shop without being packaged ready to give. Autumnal browns dressed with oranges and earthy neutrals lead on to bleak winter blacks, silvers and greys highlighted with a touch of red, which in turn might give way to soft tissue-paper yellows, greens and pinks in spring. With all this thought given to enticing customers across the threshold and to concluding each transaction so beautifully, you can now begin to imagine the calibre of the ever-changing stock.

You might find antique French doors, shutters and mirrors lining the walls; stylish urns and planters from Belgium and the Netherlands; quality garden tools sourced from as far afield as New Zealand; enormous lead cisterns or delicate china vases decorated by hand in England. There's always a smattering of well-chosen gardening books and a scattering of conservatory cushions and furniture, while tempting presents of potted bulbs and scented candles sit alongside commanding presences of stone obelisks and sphinxes. To secure something really unique, there's a local carpenter and joiner on call to custom-make tables, planters and ornamental trelliswork to whatever size and specification you desire.

If there's one difficulty with The Potting Shed, it's never what to buy, it's what not to buy.

RICHARD CHARTERS

PRODUCTS INCLUDE:
- Bird-baths
- Bread crocks
- Bulb pots
- Flowerpots
- Garden bowls
- Garden vases
- Half pots
- Herb pots
- Rhubarb forcers
- Strawberry pots
- Tiles
- Wall pots

Richard Charters
Biteabout Farm
Lowick
Berwick-upon-Tweed
Northumberland
TD15 2QE
01289 388 273
Visitors by appointment

After taking a foundation course in Art and Design at Sunderland Polytechnic, Richard Charters graduated in Three Dimensional Design from West Surrey College, then spent a further four years in the area at A Harris and Son of Wrecclesham. Established back in 1873 by Absolom Harris, and the last continuously working Victorian gardenware and craft pottery in the UK, it was eventually to succumb to ruin as the result of cheap foreign imports. In the time Richard was there he had the opportunity to make really big pots on a daily basis, mastering traditional techniques and honing his skills. He returned to the north for a spell at Errington Reay in Hexham, then travelled extensively round Europe visiting potters and potteries and fuelling the desire to work for himself. In 1991 he finally set up in his own right at an old blacksmith's forge he rented near Alnwick, and there he received the accolade of being made a professional member of the prestigious Craft Potters Association.

Richard moved in 2002 to a seven-acre smallholding of his own where he is already coppicing birch to provide a renewable source of fuel for his kiln. His clay is prepared, or 'wedged', by foot prior to being thrown on the home-built momentum kickwheel, constructed mainly from scrap material, and designed to bear a heavy load. Surface decoration is applied a day or so after potting, then, once thoroughly dried out on racks, the finished wares are fired at approximately 1000°C (1800°F), thus rendering them frost-proof, while various stoking techniques are employed to coax flame patterns on to their surface.

Richard maintains stocks of beautifully proportioned, conventionally sized pottery, but large pots are a passion and when called upon to do so he has produced truly astonishing pieces for public restoration projects and for private stately homes. Besides skills which date back through the centuries, besides the refined eye of an artist, this kind of work requires a great deal of strength and stamina to pull off. In consequence of all this it has an almost magnetic presence in the garden.

Large or small, Richard welcomes commissions for specialized and bespoke work of all kinds – from pots customized with initials or house names, through ornate decorative pieces, to reproductions of antique and ancient pots from photographs or originals.

SOLID SOUL
FURNITURE DESIGN

PRODUCTS INCLUDE:
Tractor tyre seating
Wood and concrete benches
Arched concrete chairs

Solid Soul Furniture Design
High Hazel Hall
Clapham
Lancaster
LA2 8HN
01524 251 500
www.solidsoul.moonfruit.com
Works to commission

In my travels around the country in search of quality gardenwares I have to admit that there's been an awful lot of *déjà vu* all over again. Now, I don't believe in reincarnation – and I didn't the last time I was here – but there's something extraordinary going on in the Solid Soul workshop. Brothers Kieron and Brendan McSherry are involved in a radical transfiguration of the commonplace.

We're all familiar with the municipal concrete and timber bench. Two erect aggregate end-pieces have slots to accommodate horizontal wooden slats which form a curved seat and a gently arched back rest. This is all very well, all very ergonomic. Given concrete and given wood as materials to build a seat with, none of us could do any better. Right? Wrong!

Solid Soul has a bench – with themes and variations – the like of which you've never seen before. One single swerving arc of triangular cross-sectioned concrete makes up the front legs, the arms and the back. The seat and back leg(s) is/are a curved sheet of exterior-grade plywood. Not only is the effect exquisitely sculptural, but the piece is so well balanced and well thought out that the concrete appears almost to float for want of support. You really have to walk round it and round it again, and to question, and to wonder. Some seats are made with a large or a small circular cut-out, others have slashed ribs, others still have a generous arc at the back.

For their tractor-tyre chairs the brothers simply halve a recycled tyre to produce four sturdy legs and two curving arms, then use these to support a central wooden seat.

These boys are going places. Catch them while you can afford to. Remember what Picasso did with a bicycle seat and its handlebars...

STAPLEY WATER GARDENS

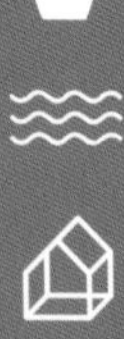

WATER-GARDEN PRODUCTS INCLUDE:
- Aquariums
- Aquatic plants
- Biological & ultraviolet filter systems
- Cold-water & tropical fish
- Fountains
- Irrigation systems
- Mist generators
- Pond liners
- Pool filters
- Pumps
- Thermometers
- Underwater lights
- Water plants
- Waterfall units

PRODUCTS INCLUDE:
- Barbecues
- Bird-baths
- Bird houses
- Bird tables
- Children's gardening kits
- Conservatories
- Conservatory & garden furniture
- Parasols
- Paving materials
- Sheds
- Sundials
- Weathervanes

Stapeley Water Gardens
Stapeley
Nantwich
Cheshire
CW5 7LH
01270 623 868
www.stapeleywatergardens.com
Open: Summer Mon – Sat 9 – 6
(Wed 9 – 8)
Sun 10 – 4
Winter Mon – Fri 9 – 5
Sat 10 – 5
Sun 10 – 4

Embracing everything from a large informal lake with waterlilies floating on the surface to a small formal pool swimming with goldfish; from a tall and powerful fountain to a little burbling brook; and from a naturalistic haven for aquatic wildlife to a futuristic and highly engineered courtyard ornament; 'water gardening' can take many forms. As interest has soared, then so the range and quality of equipment has increased, and in real terms, prices have gone down.

Where ponds and water features were once seen either as high-brow luxuries or as low-brow novelties, they are now universally considered essential elements of contemporary garden design. They bring life, movement and colour. They can generate sound, they catch and reflect the light, they create drama. The only downside to all this is that it can be very hard work indeed to decide precisely what you want.

Stapeley Water Gardens has a vast display of working water features. There are well-established pools in a variety of styles, and the staff are able to give advice and information on all the plants, fish and electrical equipment on offer. You can compare and contrast different looks here, and you can shop around for new ideas like nowhere else in the UK.

You'll find fountains that pirouette and ones that froth with bubbles like geysers. You'll find solar-powered pumps; you'll find underwater lights to illuminate a pool by night. You'll find biological and ultraviolet filter systems. You'll find low-tech tripwires to keep herons at bay and you'll find high-tech mist generators that are the height of sophistication.

On top of all this, there's a huge garden centre and an angling superstore for sea- and freshwater-fishermen (though herons attempting to cheat are politely turned away at the door). There's also (for an admission fee) a tropical oasis called The Palms where all sorts of exotic plants and wildlife thrive in the hot and humid air.

Compared to anywhere else in the UK, Scotland has the longest winters and the shortest summers so the gardening season is a short one. This makes it all the more keenly appreciated. There is an emphasis here on comfortable seating for taking the air on sunny days and for taking in the view, and there's a sensible approach to sheltering from the elements when conditions aren't all that could be wished for.

The award-winning tree-houses built by John Harris' company, Peartree, are the most enchanting hideaways imaginable. You can follow the sun's rays with Ian McGregor's finely crafted wheelbarrow benches, and the subtle intricacies of Nigel Bridges' joinery will distract and absorb the technically-minded long after their interest in the garden itself has waned. The hand-crafted French and Italian terracotta pots that Catriona Mclean brings back to her base in Dumfriesshire are acclaimed throughout the UK.

Who knows, when it would otherwise be too cold to sit outside, perhaps the Big Park's ambitions for blankets and heaters will come into their own. Whether these catch on or not, or whether more old-fashioned means of keeping warm continue to hold sway, only time will tell.

SCOTLAND

THE BIG PARK
the big park
73
OPEN

PRODUCTS INCLUDE:
Ball chairs
Barbecues
Baskets
Blankets
Children's gardening kits
Concrete furniture
Cretan pottery
Flame torch lights
Metal planters
Moroccan lanterns
Ornamental trellising
Patio heaters
Powder-coated planters
Sculpture
Seed kits
String & twine
Wall-mounted parasols
Watering cans
Wire lanterns

The Big Park
73 Dublin Street
Newtown
Edinburgh
EH3 6NS
0131 558 9360
www.thebigpark.com
Open: Tue – Sat 10 – 6

Not only does Pete Mullin have a thriving landscape architecture practice in the city, he also lectures on the subject at Edinburgh College of Art. The man knows his stuff, and likes to share his enthusiasm with others. His wife René has a marketing and retail background, so combining forces to open a shop for gardeners was a very natural step to take. They opened their doors in 2002, and the timing was just about right.

There is a long history of apartment dwelling in the Scottish capital, so gardening *per se* is not the commonest leisure pursuit here, and on account of the nippy weather people are perhaps more accustomed to getting fresh air into their lungs by promenading the many parks and public greens than by simply sitting out of doors on their balconies and patios. Nevertheless, the winds of change are blowing on the design front…

Having decorated their homes to death, many people are looking at their outside spaces afresh, wondering how to develop them to extra effect, so demand is burgeoning for intriguing modern garden furniture, for stylish pots, and for ornament of all kinds. In a secret, up-and-coming shopping enclave just a couple of minutes walk from fashionable George Street and from ultra-smart Harvey Nichols in St Andrew's Square, The Big Park is now the place to head for.

Pete's Irish grandfather gave names to all his fields and one in particular stuck in his mind. Not only does The Big Park bring back happy childhood memories, but in the context of his practice and the shop it also has connotations of the whole of the outdoors as a fun place to be, with all sorts of things to see and do. To kindle the interest of young and old alike you'll find sculpture in wood and bark, dinky wee seed kits and tools for budding gardeners, funky Finn Stone ball chairs for trendy professionals and exclusive ranges of concrete furniture and metal planters designed by Pete himself.

On trips to Scandinavia, René noticed how cafés kept their outdoor spaces open in winter by installing really powerful patio heaters and by putting blankets on all of the chairs for customers: 'People just sit down and wrap themselves up then carry on as normal.' Realizing that if people had the accessories over here, the idea would be bound to catch on in gardens, she not only sourced the hardware but introduced a fabulous range of really thick and luxurious Danish blankets. Practising what she preaches, René is often to be found snuggled up in one of her favourites, typing out orders for more stock on her laptop.

CATRIONA MCLEAN

PRODUCTS INCLUDE:
Anduze vases
Copper & zinc planters
Le Prince Jardinier tools & clothing
St Jean de Fos terracotta
Wirework furniture & screens

Catriona McLean
Sanquhar House
Sanquhar
Dumfriesshire
DG4 6JL
01659 50282
www.catrionamclean.com
Viewing by appointment

Some people just have too much talent and too much energy. Catriona McLean is both a retailer and a wholesaler of some of the highest-quality gardening products around. Not only does she personally source wares from leading manufacturers in the UK, France, Italy and Turkey, she also designs and produces ranges of her own. Her collections are exported all over the world and are especially well received in the States and in Japan, where they are recognized as representing the very best in European style – both ancient and modern. As if all this weren't enough, she divides her time in the UK between her Scottish base at Sanquhar House in the Southern Uplands and her concession at the upmarket Chelsea Gardener down south in Sydney Street, London. At the one she has her studio, offices, showroom and display garden, at the other she masterminds the beautifully kitted-out shop now selling all the tools, clothing and lifestyle accessories of le Prince Jardinier – that's Prince Louis Albert de Broglie to you.

Catriona's Mediterranean pots come in two ranges and are to die for. The urns and vases from St Jean de Fos in the Montpellier region of France are handcrafted to designs from the sixteenth and seventeenth centuries when there were up to 70 potters operating in the one small village. So authentically reproduced are the blue, green, yellow or red glazed terracotta pots they could well be mistaken for antique pieces – especially those which are artfully distressed before leaving the factory. From a small town near Nîmes, the Anduze vases date back to the Middle Ages when they adorned the gardens of the nobility. In the same way that the planting of lavender and rosemary lends an instant *je ne sais quoi*, both types of pottery have the curious gift of bestowing instant age as well as respectability on a garden.

Bringing things right up to date, Catriona's own hexagonal and square metal planters in either zinc or copper are substantial in appearance yet quite lightweight and easy to lift, so are perfect for roof gardens and balconies. Some are a witty post-modern take on traditional stacking terracotta, while others have a sleek modern profile.

Combining the best of both worlds, the metal tables and chairs here pay homage to the past but forsake the curlicues of the Victorians and Edwardians for a dashing wrap-around of galvanized wire which makes them ideal for clean-lined contemporary settings.

Most extraordinary of all though, because these seemingly disparate ranges are brought together by a single discerning eye, you'll find that they all complement each other perfectly. My best compliments to Catriona.

IAN MCGREGOR
Iain McGregor Designs
Greenbank
West End
Gordon
Berwickshire
TD3 6JP
01573 410 277
Open: Mon – Fri 9 – 5
Other times by appointment

PRODUCTS INCLUDE:
Backless benches
Chairs & carvers
Circular seats
Coffee tables
Curved benches
High-backed benches & chairs
Refectory tables
Round tables
Tree seats
Wheel benches

If a job's worth doing, it's worth doing well. Perhaps because of my own Borders ancestry, there's something I really relate to in the patience, the quiet diligence and the thoughtfulness of the Caledonian mind. Iain McGregor uses only mature timber for his furniture, most of it between 250 and 400 years old, and harvested in Scotland from estates with a managed forestry policy for renewal. He selects the trees himself (after training in engineering and agriculture he worked for years in forestry) and has them milled locally. Instead of kiln-drying the timber for speed, it is air-dried for four to six years before use. With all this attention given to the raw materials, you can well imagine how much of Iain's heart and soul goes into the design and construction of each bench, chair and table.

In a rather sad, self-fulfilling prophecy the British all too often make false economies where garden furniture is concerned. Thinking that they'll barely get a couple of months' wear out of it each year, people all too often buy cheap and poorly designed seating which is then tucked up rather shamefacedly against the house so it doesn't spoil the view. As the nights draw in it is consigned to a shed and forgotten about until the following summer. Two months' use if they're lucky. What a shame. Now, I guarantee that if you buy comfortable, durable and attractive furniture like Iain's, which you are proud to have on permanent show in a handsome setting, then you will get genuine utility and pleasure from it all year round. And it will pay you back in no time at all.

On a mellow autumn evening, why not relax in one of Iain's Kelso, Edinburgh, Stirling or Glasgow seats, a tumbler of whisky at your side on the generous flat armrests. In winter you could admire the architectural lines of their handsome high backs, itching for those bright spring mornings when you can cradle your coffee mug while listening to the birds.

Besides offering a very wide range of his own designs, Iain is happy to create replicas of worn-out but well-loved benches brought in by clients. Any length is possible, normal and high backs can be interchanged. And to help you whittle down the choice, besides maintaining a good display of ready-for-sale stock at the workshop, Iain has a full range of half-scale models – 'apprentice pieces' – for inspection so you can appreciate the full glory of all his work in the round before deciding on your commission.

LOUISE KERR

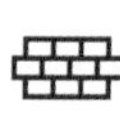

CRAFTS INCLUDE:
Basketry
Dry-stone work
Hazel & willow gates
Heather ropework
Living willow sculpture
Moss tapestry
Pebble mosaics
Tile mosaics
Willow weaving

Louise Kerr
1/2 of 10 Peinchorran
Braes
by Portree
Isle of Skye
IV51 9LL
01478 650 338
Works to commission

Scottish islanders have long been accustomed to turning their hands to different trades, calling on old skills when asked to do so and acquiring new ones as necessary. Landscape designer and craftswoman Louise Kerr carries on this grand tradition in artistic vein by producing a diverse range of artefacts and installations for the garden, exploring wherever possible the properties of locally occurring natural materials, and drawing inspiration from the scenery and history all around her on Skye.

Louise originally trained in three-dimensional design at art college, focusing on interiors. Realizing that she actually preferred external to internal works after spending a number of years in an architectural practice, she eventually branched out as a landscaper in her own right. She now thrives on the variety in her professional life and on all the creative challenges she sets herself, gaining enormous job satisfaction as projects come alive under her very own hands.

Fine penwork at a drawing board, either laying out plans for a garden or designing a feature such as a mosaic made of pebbles or broken tiles, ultimately gives way to the actual construction. There have been serpentine dry-stone walls forming raised beds in the shape of Celtic knots. There have been fences of heather rope, hurdles in willow and hazel, and wonderful spiralling pea supports exploiting the bright colours of young withies. There have also been spectacular chairs and waterside bowers woven in living willow.

Entering or leaving a garden should give pause for thought: this is something that Louise recognizes by creating extraordinarily beautiful wooden gates whose outer frame might hold a spider's web artwork of hazel and willow or whose struts might simply be naturally curving young branches, their bark intact.

When the Drumlanrig estate in Dumfries and Galloway needed replacement decorative ceiling panels for a Victorian summerhouse under restoration, Louise was uniquely placed to help. The craft origins of these intriguing tapestries in cream and green moss are shrouded in mystery and the venture was a leap into the unknown that only she was capable of taking. Louise found the work fascinating, and the results speak for themselves. Rather than rest on her laurels though, she is now keen to use mosswork in a modern setting. Any takers out there?

NIGEL
BRIDGES

PRODUCTS INCLUDE:
Benches
Bird-baths
Chairs
Driftwood furniture
Sculpture
Summer-houses
Tables

Nigel Bridges
No 1 Cottage
Magdalenehall Farm
St Boswells
Melrose
TD6 0EB
01835 822 818
www.nigelbridges.com
Works to commission

Nigel Bridges is a cabinet maker and artist craftsman whose indoor and outdoor commissions may incorporate any or all of the skills of turning, carving, inlay and lettering. As a young boy he was always encouraged to use the tools in his father's workshop. At school he was one of the last generation to be given a proper education in woodwork and throughout his six-year spell in the army – which included active service with the Royal Marines in the Falklands War – carpentry was to be a much-valued leisure pursuit.

He firmly believes that you can teach yourself anything if you set your mind to it and that, where a practical subject is concerned, there's no substitute at all for simply getting on and doing it. I hope the pupils at Edinburgh College of Art who were lucky enough to have him as a lecturer took this philosophy to heart. Practice makes perfect.

His straightforward, pragmatic approach has meant that while becoming technically highly proficient, Nigel has acquired an instinctive rapport with wood as a raw material. The result is that apparently simple pieces of his work have an innate sophistication; highly complex works have a refreshing air of ease and assurance about them.

A commission to produce a bird-bath for a Chinese garden resulted in Nigel procuring an elegantly flared section from the trunk of an elm and carving out a hollow that looks as though it might have been formed by nature. He chose elm because it is so impervious to rot that the Romans even used it for water pipes. Other more formal bird-baths by Nigel have used turned yew, burr elm and lead. A challenge from friends while walking by the Tweed led to the construction of some beguiling seats using only driftwood from the riverbank.

Invited by Edinburgh's prestigious Scottish Gallery to reinvent the conventional bench for one of its outdoor exhibitions, he created an exquisite piece inscribed 'fragments of time like petals in the garden spent'. Rather than having its legs four-square on the ground, it derives its strength and stability from end pieces with a triangular construction influenced by the shape of a traditional grass scythe. As if that weren't enough, his attention to hidden detail is such that he devised special mortise-and-tenon joints with sloping shoulders to limit water seepage and consequently reduce the risk of frost damage in icy winters.

Bringing his skill and ingenuity to the fore, the circular Gregg Summerhouse, made for a garden in the conservation village of Dryburgh, is a showcase of his talent. Made without a single nail or screw from the timber of eleven butts of oak, it has a turret with curved windows topped with a dovecote. The main body, double-skinned for insulation, has a flexible seating system that can be rearranged to form a romantic sleeping platform for two.

THE ORKNEY STONE COMPANY

PRODUCTS INCLUDE:
Mirrors
Pebble fountains
Platters
Tables
Wash basins
Water features

The Orkney Stone Company
Viewfield
Church Road
South Ronaldsay
Orkney
KW17 2SR
01856 831 462
www.orkneystone.com
Works to commission

There is a history of stone working here that goes back to the beginnings of time. The 70 or so islands and islets of the Orkneys were the Orcades of classical literature, and standing stones, circles, underground and earth houses dating back to the Stone and Bronze Ages remain very much in evidence to this day. Ferocious westerly gales blowing unimpeded across the Atlantic made shelter of the utmost necessity to early man, but also accounted for the general scarcity of trees and therefore of wood for building, so the tough and hard-wearing sedimentary sandstone of the islands has always been a much-valued commodity.

Albert Scott hails originally from North Ronaldsay, which is the smallest and most north-easterly outpost of the archipelago, but now lives much closer to the mainland on South Ronaldsay. Here, along with his artist wife Louise, he formed the Orkney Stone Company in the year 2000.

Making contemporary pieces with a timeless appeal, often working to commissions, one of the company's main objectives is the continued use, wherever possible, of traditional skills and craftsmanship. All the stone, which has beautiful pattern and texture, is selected and hand quarried by Albert himself, then shaped into the most amazing mirrors, tables, platters, wash basins, outdoor shower trays and garden water features.

Using simple splitting chisels forged by a blacksmith, Albert carefully clefts open the stone along one of its gently coloured brown or grey layers to reveal its inner beauty, then turns and grinds it to his will. The contrast between the worked and unworked surfaces of each piece – the rough exterior rim of a bowl, say, and its polished interior – brings out the full character of the stone. No two pieces are ever quite the same, as the inherent qualities of each quarried slab will inform the final outcome.

Albert has made vessels well over a metre in diameter for use as poolside shower trays, as overflowing water features and as self-contained pebble fountains. Their wide rims can be inscribed with lettering, or the rough stone can be left to speak across the ages in a voice all its own.

PEAR TREE

PRODUCTS INCLUDE:
Bunk beds
Cargo nets
Drinks decks
Flags
Hammocks
Pulleys
Rope ladders
Swings
Tree houses
Wine baskets

Pear Tree
The Stables
Maunsheugh Road
Fenwick
Ayrshire
KA3 6AN
01560 600 111
www.peartreehouse.com
Sites surveyed by appointment

Whether it's a scavenged pallet wedged precariously between some branches or the eighteenth-century 'Tudor' folly at Pitchford Hall in Shropshire atop its five-hundred-year-old lime, there's no denying the magic of a tree-house. On a fantasy level we all have memories of Winnie-the-Pooh's home in a hollowed-out tree trunk and of the Swiss Family Robinson's driftwood fortress among the palms. Then somewhere deep, dark and atavistic inside ourselves we also share early man's reverence for trees as places of refuge from our enemies and of shelter from the elements. In the twenty-first century tree-houses are places of peace and tranquillity for adults and of creative play for children. For both they give a wonderful sense of being apart from the everyday hubbub and of being closer to the natural world.

The first tree-house John Harris built was for his own children. Flushed with success he tentatively advertised his services in *House and Garden*. Little did he know what he was letting himself in for. His company, Pear Tree, now designs and builds tree-houses all around the world. Completed projects have included simple drinks decks, tiny playhouses, a nursery-school classroom, a mock castle, a 30-seater dining room and, for the Chelsea Flower Show, a Balinese-style tree-house with water running down the rills of each stair tread. One tree-house even included a Jacuzzi!

Ash, beech, cedar, chestnut, lime, oak and mature fruit trees provide the best foundations. If they are strong and healthy with trunks over 1.5m (5ft) in circumference then they can be the sole supporter of a tree-house. Smaller specimens and shallow-rooted trees such as poplars and silver birch may require support stilts to distribute the overall weight. Another alternative is to use several smaller trees to spread the load. And if you haven't got a tree at all, fear not! There's always the Hideaway Hollow, a free-standing Scandinavian redwood tree-trunk with a spiral staircase leading to a covered veranda.

Out of concern for the environment, Pear Tree buys timber only from sustainable forestry, endeavouring to use only water-based preservatives, and recycling all waste material.

Plans always allow for the growth of your tree and any necessary adjustments to each designed structure are made as part of the company's annual maintenance programme.

ARABELLA LENNOX-BOYD MIC
JANE NORTHUMBERLAND DAV
DEBORAH DEVONSHIRE ANDY
STEPHEN WOODHAMS ANGEL
ARABELLA LENNOX-BOYD MIC
CLARE FOSTER DAVID HESSA
ANDY MURDOCK PIPPA GREEN
MARYLYN ABBOTT EVELYN T
ANTHONY NOEL DAVID FOSTER
CLARE FOSTER PHILIP CAVE G
MARYLYN ABBOTT STEPHEN
DAVID HESSAYON JANE NORTH
PHILIP CAVE GUY COOPER & GO

HELE OSBORNE DAVID FOSTER
D HESSAYON PAMELA WOODS
MURDOCK PIPPA GREENWOOD
A CONNER MARYLYN ABBOTT
HELE OSBORNE DAVID FOSTER
ON JANE NORTHUMBERLAND
VOOD DEBORAH DEVONSHIRE
URLBY STEPHEN WOODHAMS

STATE OF THE ART

PHILIP CAVE
JY COOPER & GORDON TAYLOR
VOODHAMS ANGELA CONNER
JMBERLAND EVELYN THURLBY
RDON TAYLOR ANTHONY NOEL

Gardening is about growth and development. In design terms it is not only about flair and imagination, it is about having an eye for detail and a sense of proportion. It is also about sensitivity to place and to people, about making each garden fulfil – so far as humanly possible – the needs of everyone who will work, rest or play there.

Time spent listening to the opinions and experiences of others is always well repaid. It can help us look at things afresh, and it can spur us on to greater deeds. In the following pages you will find a variety of creative approaches to reflect upon, and there's a great deal of professional knowledge and insight to take heed of. All the interviewees have been remarkably generous.

On a personal note, it's worth mentioning that two of the interviews have actually shifted my own perspective on a couple of aspects of gardening. And that's great, because I'm always up for something new. Are you?

STATE OF THE ART

ANDY MURDOCK

Greenmount College in Northern Ireland is funded by the Department of Agriculture and Rural Development and offers a wide range of practical courses with work placements, always striving to match the skills of its students with the needs of future employers. Andy Murdock, Senior Lecturer in Horticulture, explores the sudden boom of interest in his subject area.

'A lot of students come out of Belfast as well as from rural areas to enrol on our horticulture courses. The female intake fluctuates between 5 and 8 per cent, which is very low, whereas it is about 99 per cent on the floristry side. We've spent a lot of time and money trying to recruit more actively within schools, but people still have set gender roles.

'When I studied here in 1985 there was just the one course. Now we've got 9 different programmes, and we're still looking to expand. Many students enrol for the National Diploma after GCSEs, others come in after A levels for the Higher National Diploma. Because we're very industry focused, we have a range of full- and part-time courses to build up expertize in such areas as sports grounds, parks, amenity horticulture, garden centres and in nursery stock production. We work very closely with businesses in Northern Ireland to see where we can best pitch our emphasis, holding a lot of liaison meetings to make sure we've got our finger on the pulse.

'The demand for green-keeping courses has gone through the roof, and we now have 60 part-time green-keeping places each year. There's a large skill-base out there already as we've been training people for a long time, but still they keep coming. The leisure industry has grown as the retirement age has dropped; there's diversification on large farms with land use going over to golf courses; higher and higher standards are being demanded as companies like the Hilton Hotel Group have come to Northern Ireland. Groundsmanship today offers a very good career path.

'Garden design is much in vogue and our courses are always over subscribed, but it's important to realize that people in Northern Ireland are reluctant to spend money on a plan – they actually want the work done. Clients want someone who can come in for a chat, talk them through their ideas for the garden, then come back with some men and see the job through to completion. Students who have done a practical, hands-on course are in a better position to offer that service, but they have to be aware that there's no fixed career structure in garden design and that life skills and good communication skills are vital if a business is to succeed.

'We have a 98 per cent rate of employment at the end of each academic year, and at a recent careers convention there were more vacancies on offer than there were students to fill them, which was absolutely tremendous for us. Three years ago I might have had the odd student coming back in August, still without a job. Now, I have employers phoning in May, June and July asking for students. People often have to change careers midstream, but there's a big future in horticulture as a career for life.'

For more information about Greenmount College, telephone 028 9442 6700 or visit www.greenmount.ac.uk

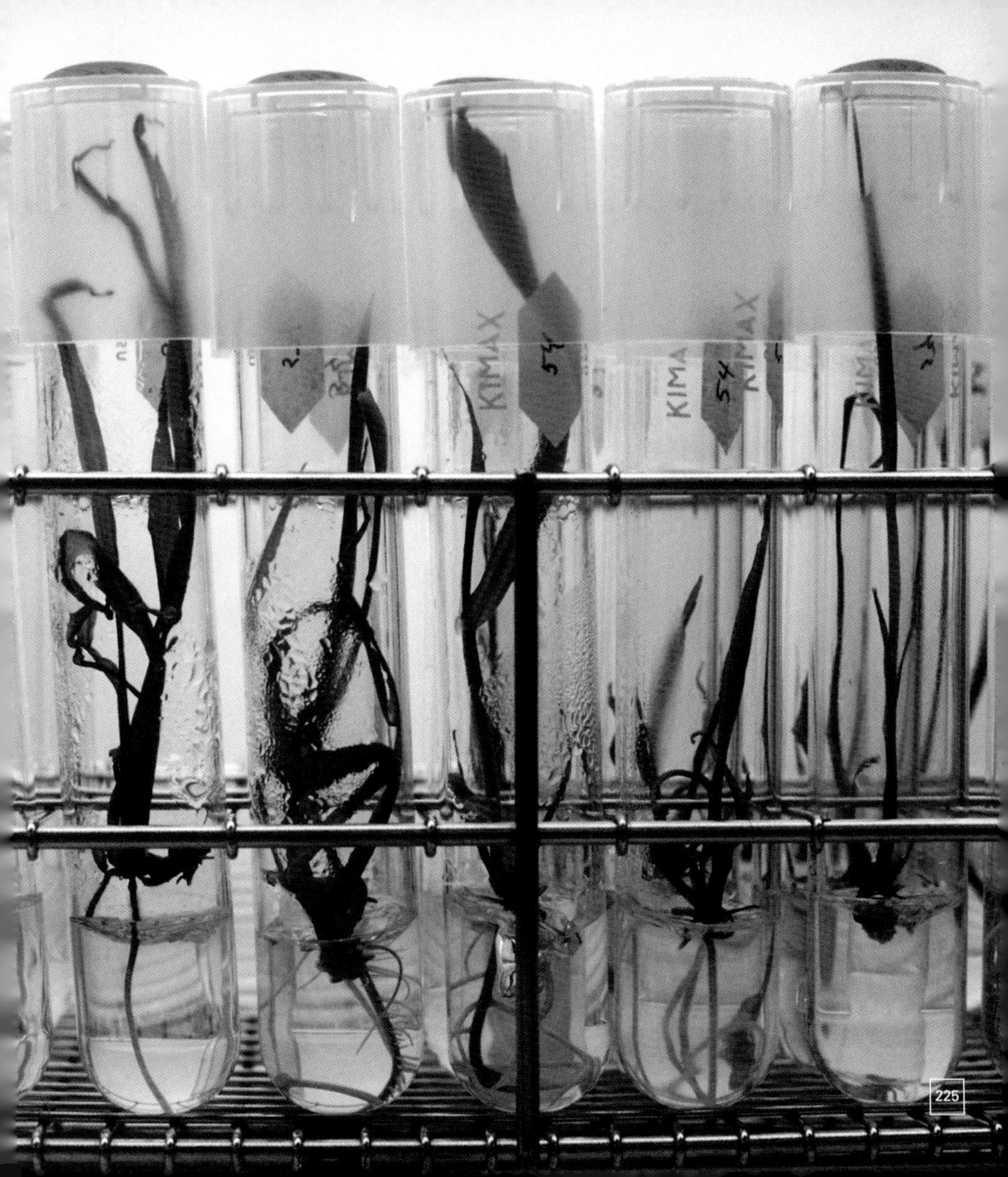
KIMAX

ANGELA CONNER

One of our great portrait sculptors, Angela Conner also makes large-scale kinetic pieces imbued with great emotional significance: segmented stone discs ripple effortlessly in the wind; shadows from jagged shards of bronze form perfect circles in the sunlight. Art, life and the elements merge seamlessly together in her work.

'We need peace and quiet as well as noise and excitement, and I think that for many centuries the garden has been looked on as something without the complications of a church but giving the same sense of rest and contemplation. And the reason for that, I'm convinced, is that it is linked with nature, which is a huge force that is manifestly powerful. We feel comforted by a garden's quiet, long-term rhythms.

'I'm not making pieces that I then place into nature, which is the norm for sculpture, but I'm using wind, or the sun's shadows, or gravity, or water to make the sculpture very gently, and intentionally very gently, move. So a piece of solid steel, or an apparently lifeless stone, or whatever material I use, becomes interwoven with nature because it uses nature to have dynamics of its own.

'Revelation at Chatsworth is all about gravity and water: the inner globe fills with water which comes from a lovely lake up on the hill – the water would be coming out through streams anyway, so it's not being wasted at all. As the globe fills it gets heavier and heavier, and because it has been made so that it can sink, it does sink, and in the action of sinking pulls the leaves up over it. Then when it is completely filled it releases the water, and there you are...

'My pieces often have an intended cycle that is actually saying something, which people might or might not pick up on. They can just look at them as pieces of sculpture and that's the end of it. But equally, if they want to know more, then they will – just by sitting and watching it. To go back to Revelation for instance, that's something every bulb does: out of this rather nicely, not that interestingly shaped bulb, comes this amazing flower. And the cycle is repeated again and again.

I like developing sculptures that are not only relevant to the site but also to the people they are for. Revelation relates to the Devonshires, who over the centuries, have supported various artists who, when they were ready, could go out to a more general public, to be shown and seen. That too is what the piece is about – the idea of holding something very, precious and then releasing it to the world.

For more information about Angela Conner's work telephone 020 7221 4510.

ANTHONY NOEL

Anthony Noel's town gardens use a perfectly judged extravagance of style to compensate for lack of space. Because his clients are leading players in the worlds of rock, pop, film and theatre, much of his finest work is hidden from the public eye. Here he shares the secret of his success and the sources of his inspiration.

In small gardens you can't really mask the boundaries, you've got to work with the walls and fences and take advantage of any borrowed landscape beyond. You've also got to go along with the shape and, although I've tried curves and circles, I think a more or less rectilinear design works best with the spirit of town gardening. If it's town, it has got to be smart. It can look old and worn, but there has to be a fundamental elegance.

I like big scale, the whole concept of which is grand in itself. Take garden urns: huge, over-scaled ones are very dramatic and so long as the lines are good and the proportions are right, you can get away with good reproductions. I use these a lot, but I always distress them. I use a hammer and chisel, then where I crack bits away I rub in dirt and yoghurt to encourage moss and lichen to grow.

Clients appreciate this attention to detail because although they like the grandeur they don't want anything to look vulgar. Even the most beautiful objects can look unsympathetic when new, especially if large and in a small space. You've got to make everything look as though God has dropped the garden from heaven, as if it has always been there.

I grew up in a 17th-century farmhouse; the floors were all over the place and everything was ancient and crumbly and wonky. Being an artistic kid I looked at other old buildings and I saw that they were invariably overgrown and mossy. I suppose I just understood the poetry of these places.

We went to visit Sissinghurst when I was nine and I met Vita Sackville-West. She was weeding in the Tower Garden. I didn't know who she was – she was quite gruff and in her gaiters and pearls, smoking. I thought she was a gardener. We started talking and in fact she was very gentle and patient, but then mother dragged me away as I was probably being a nuisance. We moved on and saw the White Garden – I was just mesmerized by it. It was a formative experience.

There's plenty of scope for fantasy in a garden, just so long as you know where it's appropriate and equally when to hold back. My advice is always to think big – when in doubt, over-scale. Remember, the sky is your ceiling in any garden and you've just got to scale about 20 times more than you think would be right.

Consider the main vista and the secondary vista, too. When you go out into a garden you want to have nice things to look at on your left and right, but you also want something to look at as you come back towards the house. I think it is really important that a garden is like sculpture: of course you've got to be able to move around in it, but it's got to have impact too, so that you want to go out there in the first place.

Perhaps above all else, I like a garden to feel cosy. Never forget that grandeur can be really, really comfortable.

For more information about Anthony Noel's work, telephone 020 7736 2907.

ARABELLA LENNOX-BOYD

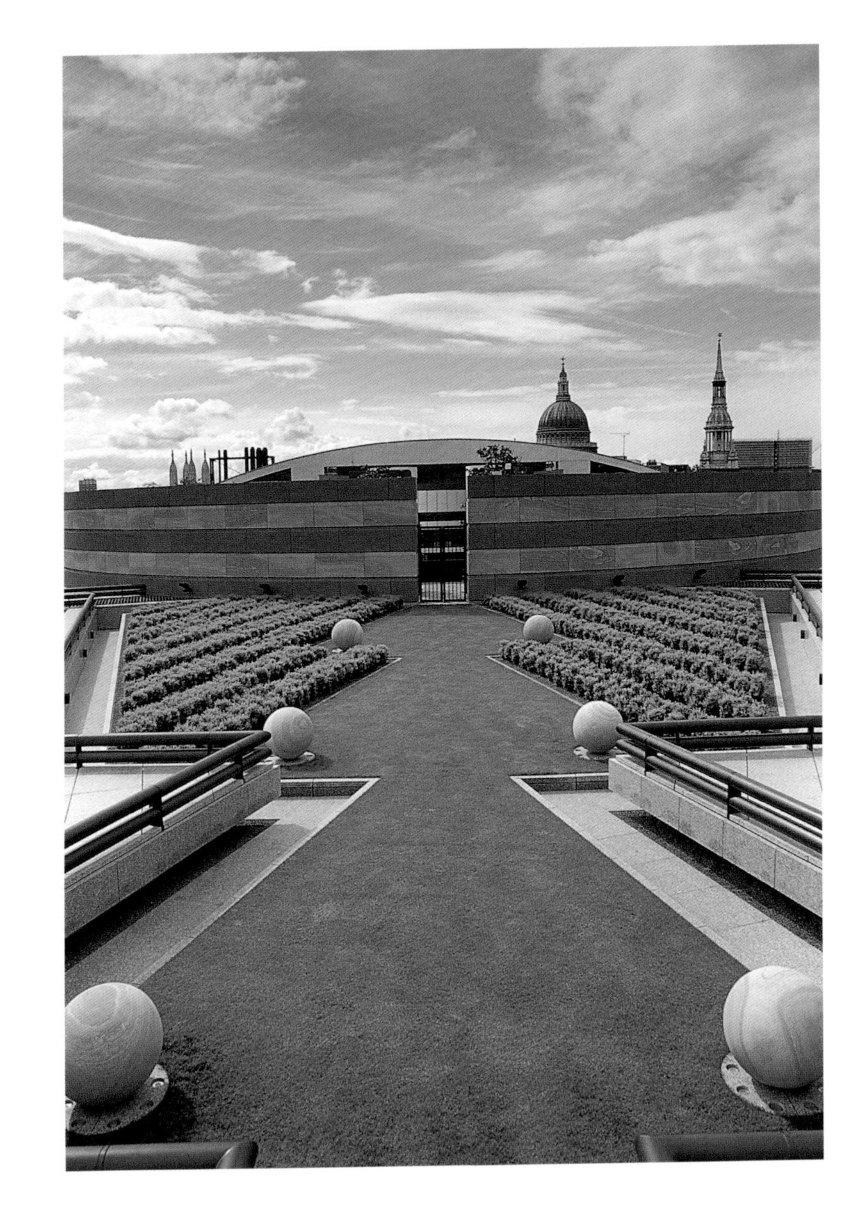

Whether she is creating an award-winning garden at Chelsea, re-imagining a courtyard, handling an historic country estate or developing a vast city-rooftop, the timeless beauty of Lady Lennox-Boyd's work is characterized by a perfect sense of scale and a sensitivity to place.

'I think that a garden should open out: it should have views out into the landscape and also be a part of it. It is so sad when a garden is hemmed in by very high hedges, it gives you no indication of where it is. Avenues of trees, or openings in hedges, or changes in level can all lead slowly out into the landscape and, conversely, draw the landscape in. I like to think of the design of a garden as having a rhythm that is much faster and more intense near the house and then fading to something a little more leisurely and relaxed towards the boundaries.

'When laying out a garden you have to look at the practical considerations – getting from A to B, then from B to C. Then you think, well, where am I going to sit, where are we going to walk, how can I join this part of a garden to that? It can be helpful to think in terms of a house. You might have a big room which is the sitting room, then you go through a corridor to the library and so on. At Stanbridge Mill in Dorset, for example, there's a lovely open space on the south-facing side of the property. From there, you go through a narrower area which is more intimate and full of flowers, a little obsessive even. Then you go round the corner through a walkway of hedges into another garden which then opens out into the view. It's all part of my initial plan, and it's all part of a story. I don't go out of my way to be modern or original. Quite simply, a garden has to fit the place, it has to fit the people, and it has to fit their requirements.

'When it comes to the Chelsea Flower Show, I hate gimmicks, and I don't like things that can't be related to real gardens. After all, you're given a proper space there, albeit a modest one, and whatever you do has to relate to that amount of space. You should be able to take it out just as it is and make it work in the real world outside.

'Scale is very, very important to me. I was brought up in Rome and I do feel that a sense of that architecture is just in me. I scrutinize things, I visit historical gardens and buildings – always taking photographs, making records, measuring. If I see a good fountain I will measure it, not only for the size but also for its proportions. I think it is important not to shy away from the past. Looking at a wonderful garden or at a perfectly beautiful fountain is a way of learning: you can try to analyse just why something is so good, then see if that can be translated into a modern context. After all, previous generations have got things so right – just look at the gardens of the Renaissance.

'There's such pressure now to design outrageously modern gardens and though I think these can be interesting, fun and set one thinking at a tangent, what I like to do myself is to create gardens that will be around for a long, long time. It's why I enjoy life so much.'

For more information about Arabella Lennox-Boyd's work, telephone Landscape and Architectural Design on 020 7931 9995, or visit arabellalennoxboyd.com

CLARE FOSTER

***Gardens Illustrated* is a resolutely upmarket magazine with an international design flavour and a passion for plants. While other adventurous journals have folded, 2003 saw *Gardens Illustrated* celebrating its tenth birthday. Editor Clare Foster examines its role in the gardener's world.**

'You have only to look at the news-stands to see the vast number of gardening magazines that readers have to choose from. There are some very good magazines telling people exactly what to do at the right time of year, so when founding editor Rosie Atkins launched *Gardens Illustrated* in 1993 it was with the deliberate intention of being different to the rest.

'We like to think of ourselves as providing inspiration rather than giving people purely practical advice. It's all about ideas and pulling back for the bigger picture rather than focusing on the nitty-gritty. Gardening isn't just about getting your hands raw and dirty, or getting your feet wet and cold – although obviously there's a lot of that. It's also about aesthetics, and about design, and art comes into it too. And I think the magazine really reflects that.

'Although words of course are terribly important, much of the inspiration comes through the pictures, so we go to a lot of trouble commissioning the shots we need. We're dealing with a highly visual subject, so Gardens Illustrated – as the title would suggest – is a very visually oriented magazine.

'The first things that I always think about are the plants. Our readership is quite diverse, from professional garden designers to amateur gardeners, to people who don't actually have a garden – what unites them all is a love of plants. There's a lot of garden design out there that uses hard-landscaping incredibly well, and more and more people are beginning to appreciate that, but plants are the primary uniting factor, and they're very much at the core of the magazine.

'Our circulation is around 32,000 at the moment but we're an up-market magazine, and to a lot of people will seem a bit out of reach, so ours is always going to be a niche readership. That said, we have a dedicated following, reflected in a very high level of subscription sales. I know a lot of readers keep all their copies for reference, which is very satisfying as magazines are generally thought of as throwaway reading.

'I think that the general public's attitude to the garden is changing. It was almost unheard of ten years ago for a private individual to employ a designer, but more and more people are using garden designers now, especially once they've settled in a place that will be home for a number of years. They're coming to terms with the fact that it is quite expensive, just as expensive – if not more so – than getting a new kitchen. But I think they're shrewd enough to realise that, like a good kitchen, a well-designed, horticulturally real garden, as opposed to a quick-fix makeover, will add value to their property in the long term as well as giving them a great deal of pleasure.'

For more information about *Gardens Illustrated* visit www.bbcworldwide.com/magazines/gardensillustrated

DAVID FOSTER

THRIVE is a national charity enabling people with illnesses and disabilities, the socially and economically disadvantaged, the young and the old, to participate fully in the life of the community through gardening. Chief executive David Foster discusses its work.

'Firstly, we are an umbrella for some 1,600 projects across the country – some we run ourselves, others we support with training, advice and information.

'The second thing we do is provide advice, support and information for people who just want to be involved in gardening as part of their leisure activity but who find this difficult – often because of growing infirmity as they get older, or through illness, accident or disability.

'Thirdly, we research how gardening can be used to support the disabled and the disadvantaged. For example, we have looked into gardening in prisons and other secure institutions, and we are examining the use of gardening in the case of people with Alzheimer's disease.

'Gardening is a wonderful tool for supporting people, and it can have remarkable results. For example, it can be an enjoyable form of physiotherapy for people recovering from a stroke. Better to prick out lettuces and take cuttings to improve your hand to eye co-ordination than to move marbles from one vase to another. Better to be outdoors in the fresh air doing occupational therapy than to be in an overheated hospital. And for people with mental health problems, gardening can be tremendously powerful in rebuilding confidence.

'I have been to hospices where the patients are gardening on tables or even on trolleys by their beds. It is quite remarkable what they get from it. They are touching and handling soil and plants, caring for living things.

'There's lots of evidence that getting close to nature is good for the soul and the mind. Even in Ancient Egypt the royal physicians would prescribe a spell in the palace gardens for people suffering from stress. In the 18th century the rules of the Dorset County Asylum required people to work in its grounds to promote cheerfulness and happiness.

'We find all too often that the medical and social care professions underestimate people's potential. People with learning disabilities come to us, and by putting them in an environment that is conducive to trying things, and by encouraging them to have a go, we find that they have greater capabilities than they were given credit for. People with enduring mental health problems often find it very difficult to hold down a job because their illness is cyclical. But with gardening it is possible to create good social enterprises run for the benefit of the people employed there. People can get involved in contract gardening or in growing produce to sell.

'We think the moment of social and therapeutic horticulture has really come. The number of projects around the country is growing all the time.'

For more information, to make a donation, or to volunteer your services, contact Thrive National Office, The Geoffrey Udall Centre, Beech Hill, Reading, Berkshire, RG7 2AT. Telephone 0118 988 5688 or visit www.thrive.org.uk To learn more about gardening in old age, see www.carryongardening.org.uk

DAVID HESSAYON

Common-sense sound advice is timeless. Which is why, at the still point of a turning world, botanist Dr Hessayon's instantly recognizable *Expert Books* are consistent bestsellers. Concept-driven, not personality-led, they will be welcome long after the TV make-over programmes have exhausted our patience.

'I don't think that the gardening scene in front of the house has changed anything like so dramatically as the media would have us believe. When I started out, gardening was already Britain's number-one outdoor hobby. And guess what? It still is. What has changed is the way that we talk about gardening, and the way it is presented on television.

'If you look at cookery magazines and programmes it's the same story. Everyone enjoys the drama and spectacle of it, but I don't honestly think that the food we serve up in the evening is influenced much – give or take a few fancy packets from the supermarket. People aren't cooking differently, but they're watching it because it's good fun.

'Gardening programmes race to finish a garden in 48 hours, though how you build a real garden in that time I don't know. For the first few days you should do nothing but walk up and down and look. Anyway, for the presenters it's all a question of will it be finished before the owners come back? What is their reaction going to be? And finally, do you really, really like what we've done? It is the game-show element, not the gardening itself that is so thrilling. Modern television must never be boring, so plants go in which are far too big and far too close together. If they were planted at the proper size and distance the end result wouldn't arouse enough interest.

'In real life, there isn't a vast amount of steel or concrete or decking, and when there's something to do or something's gone wrong, the demand is still there for straightforward hard instruction. That's why people still turn to the printed word.

'The *Expert Books* are about pulling all the facts together and then presenting them clearly. The style is simple and didactic. If I've repeated myself, then fine, it was worth saying twice. If I've ended a sentence with a preposition, that's great, so did Churchill. If there's a rawness about it, that's what I want. There's a danger in things getting so polished and honed that you lose all sense of immediacy.

'I did all my own layouts when I started the series. I was my own editor and my own publisher too, so I didn't have to please anybody except the man or the woman in the semi-detached across the road. The books' success comes down to the fact that they're giving people information without trying to impress. Also, I don't think you could tell by looking at the books what I liked. In the nicest possible way it's none of your business. Similarly, what you like is none of mine. Whether you're reading the *Bulb Expert*, or the *Flower Expert*, I'll describe a plant, give you its good and bad points, then I'll leave you to choose.

'I'm not writing for designers, for critics, or to win a prize. I am writing for ordinary people who pay me that great compliment: "with all due respect Dr Hessayon, I could have done that". You see, there's no great gap between us: I'm simply sharing my notebooks with them.'
For more details, visit your local bookshop.

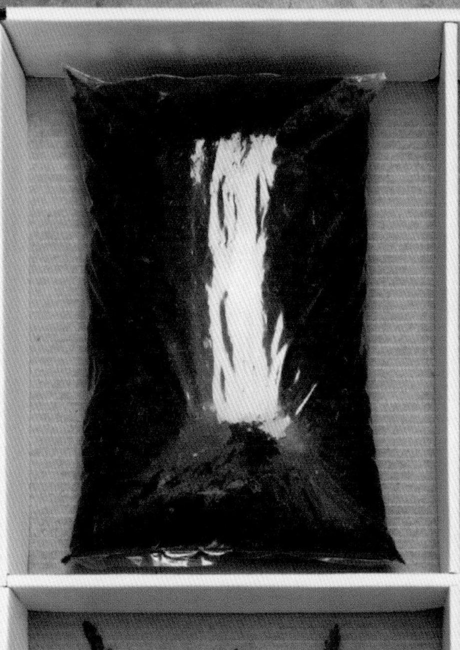
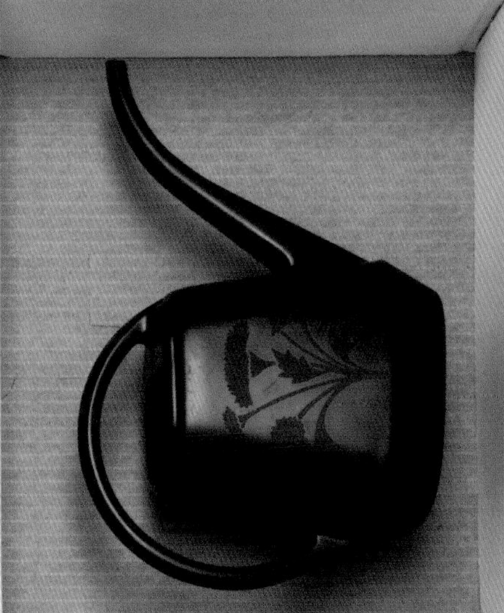

DEBORAH
DEVONSHIRE

There can be no doubt that it is more interesting to see a great house and garden that is lived in and loved than to visit somewhere that is empty and just looked at for a few hours a day. Chatsworth in Derbyshire, seat of the Dukes of Devonshire, while steeped in history, also has an eye to the future. Farm shops sell estate produce, the household carpenters produce exquisite garden furniture and there is a vigorous education programme to help close the gap between town and country. A large team of outdoor staff is employed in maintaining and restoring existing features, while world-class artists and architects continue making their mark on the estate under the patronage of the eleventh Duke and Duchess.

'Chatsworth came into the Cavendish family in about 1550 through Bess of Hardwick, and the garden has been subject to a variety of fashions and to the work of many influential gardeners over the centuries. First of all Bess of Hardwick had an orchard and a place to keep roebuck for the table. Then London and Wise, who were pupils of Le Nôtre came to help the first Duke make it very formal indeed. That was in the late 1690s and early 1700s: it must have been an astonishment to people coming to this part of the country, which was pretty wild then, to find this elaborate Louis XIV style garden – when Hampton Court was being restored a few years ago, the designs in the archives here were used for reference.

'The next Duke began to feel it should be a little less customized, so some of the really formal parts were undone and ordinary forest trees were planted in the garden. William Kent was a great friend of Lord Burlington, whose daughter married the fourth Duke of Devonshire, so all those influences came in. With the rise of the Romantic Movement, Capability Brown was brought in around 1760, removing all the wonderful terraces and replacing them with a huge sweeping lawn, making the garden almost like the park.

'Things remained like that until the Bachelor Duke engaged Joseph Paxton as head gardener in 1826, when an incredible era of progress began. Gardeners were sent all over the world to bring back rare and exotic plants for which Paxton built his amazing glasshouses, in one of which the giant Victoria regina waterlily flowered for the first time in Britain. Then in the 1840s the Emperor Fountain astonished visitors with what was then by far the tallest jet in the world.

'This place has always been open to the public – it's a tradition here, and in the middle of the nineteenth century there were already around 80,000 visitors every summer. People are always welcome and they can walk in the park without any charge day or night, winter or summer. It's a real pleasure to see them.'

For more information on Chatsworth House and Garden, telephone 01246 565 300 or visit www.chatsworth.org
To commission garden furniture from Chatsworth Carpenters call 01246 565 371.

EVELYN THURLBY

Former Chief Executive of The Eden Project, Evelyn Thurlby is now Chief Operations Director of the National Botanic Garden of Wales. Formation mowing teams tend the lawns, and 2003 saw the great glasshouse illuminated as a giant red nose for Comic Relief. Clearly not a stuffy enterprise...

'Our mission is to be a progressive, botanic garden that communicates the story of plants and the need for conservation. iWe know plants are important, that life on earth could not exist without them, yet the general public doesn't always grasp this, and scientists mask the issue with words such as "biodiversity" and "sustainability". Our aim is to create an experience that is friendly and accessible, with no dumbing down.

'What we're all about is our living collection and we use straightforward ground rules for our selection criteria. We embrace our Welsh connection, taking on the conservation of rare and endangered native species and linking this into the bigger world picture. We are on the site of an eighteenth-century water park, so we look at the relationship between plants and water. We are also concerned about maintaining the natural status quo through such things as composting, mulching and recycling.

'Plant origins are important, and we look at the stories of the plant hunters to awaken people to the fact that flowers growing naturally in our gardens can be traced back to all parts of the globe. This is about showing that rhododendrons come from China, not England. We also look at plant classification to show the botanical relationships within plant families, but rather than presenting our beds like allotments, we lay them out like miniature gardens at the Chelsea Flower Show. We place a colossal emphasis on aesthetics because traditional botanic gardens don't necessarily respond to the modern public's greater visual awareness.

'Art is also important to us. Not only have we got fantastic water sculptures by William Pye and Marion Kalmus but Exploration 2003 saw 12 international artists and makers creating site-specific installations around the estate.

'In the great glasshouse designed by Sir Norman Foster we feature seven distinct geographical areas from the Mediterranean climate. We employed Kathryn Gustafson to master-plan the internal landscape to be as close as possible to an actual representation of plants in their natural setting. There are banks and slopes, gabion walls and limestone rockfaces. To control the environment we've installed a building management system in charge of humidity, watering, lighting and temperature.

'In spite of the technology, we're not about controlling people. You won't find a single "Keep off the Grass" sign. We've created a living willow play area for children, and there'll be a water labyrinth too. We give visitors absolute freedom to gain whatever they want to. It's not about lecturing people, but creeping up behind them and whispering gently in their ear.'

For more information about The Eden Project telephone 01558 668 768, or visit www.gardenofwales.org.uk

GUY COOPER &
GORDON TAYLOR

Through their books, television series and lectures, Guy Cooper and Gordon Taylor have attained international recognition as leading commentators on cutting-edge gardens. As partners in Landscape Design Ltd they have created outdoor spaces all over the world. Here, they discuss the concept of making design relevant to your particular environment.

GT Landscape designers such as Kathryn Gustafson, George Hargreaves and Robert Irwin, who are well known for working on a site-generated basis, are mainly involved in large public projects. To find a series of site-generated incidents in a private garden is extremely unusual, so Jessica Duncan's garden in Devon is quite a rarity.
GC People are so used to imposing what they think a garden should be about on their plot. Rather than looking at the place, then responding to its potential, they'll just say: 'Well, my garden is so wide, so long, I like the following flowers, I like the following shrubs – this is what I'll have.'
GT They're not using their imagination. Jessica's is such a wonderful example of site-generated design because she's doing the ultimate to adapt what she found on a former dairy farm to her own use, and to adopt it into the landscape. For example, some roofless outbuildings now form a sheltered place for tender subjects. Also the concrete floor of a milking parlour was too thick and too heavy to remove easily, so Mediterranean plants have been used to colonise the spaces and the cracks, and Jessica has established a golden honeysuckle hedge around it from which she is encouraging some leaping hare topiary. The whole thing acts as a platform from which to view the garden.
GC Beyond the land she owns are fields, so she has created a vista running down into the wooded garden, which then leads the eye up through a break in the perimeter planting to this borrowed landscape beyond. You're intrigued, and you want to walk there.
GT At one point a favourite hill is seen both over and through a young hedge of dogwood cuttings, the outline of which echoes the profile of the hill. A curved run or two of woven willow physically reinforces the stems and visually enhances the effect.
GC Further along the same hedgerow there's a trellis with a large circular cut-out framing another view of the hill. By the end of the walk you've encountered all the things to be seen, such as the shallow reflecting pool formed out of the old slurry lagoon and the foot labyrinth she made from reclaimed cobbles.
GT Of course, we're all indebted to Pope's admonition to 'consult the genius of the place' and there has long been the notion of a progress or preferred route through a garden. 18th-century English landscape design owed a lot to Italy and so much since has been a pastiche or a re-working of one style or another. I'm not suggesting that the site-generated approach should be the only one, but it is the one truly original approach to garden design to have emerged out of the latter part of the 20th century. Perhaps today's designers should consult the contemporary genius of each place when seeking out the shapes and the patterns that will inform their work in the 21st century.

For more information about Guy Cooper and Gordon Taylor's work, telephone 020 7584 7583.

JANE NORTHUMBERLAND

The wife of a second son, the Duchess of Northumberland never expected to find herself mistress of such a large estate. Archaeological surveys of more or less derelict ground at Alnwick Castle revealed the accumulated layers of no fewer than seven historical gardens. Realizing that this made any attempt at restoration an impossible conundrum, her forward-looking and altruistic approach has not only helped reinvigorate the local economy, it has aroused the attention of gardeners around the globe.

'I felt really strongly at the beginning of the project that by pulling together a whole team of experts, it should be possible to create something as good as anything that had been created two-hundred years ago. This was considered a rather arrogant viewpoint by some of the historians and official bodies we consulted, but the more I thought about it the more I thought, this is just ridiculous.

'A lot of people in England have said, 'Oh, she's just making a theme park. But I don't think that's right – although I would agree that it's not a straightforward garden in any conventional sense.

'I was creating a visitor attraction, so it was no good just making a beautiful garden as an adjunct to the castle. I had to create something that would be loved for generations, and I felt that water would be the means of achieving that. I felt sure it was possible to incorporate state-of-the-art water technology within a classically designed garden.

'It's a big gamble doing something on this scale, but I had to raise a lot of money and I was determined it was going to be built and that I'd stick with it.

'Everyone involved in the garden at Alnwick has worked as part of a team: Wirtz International interpreted the original vision; Ritchie MacKenzie, a Glasgow-based engineering company, have made the water come alive; and I've been talking to a major lighting company about making it look fantastic by night and in the winter.

'The knock-on effect has been enormous. Of course, everything in the North East is buzzing at the moment with the regeneration of Newcastle and Gateshead. But what happened in the summer of 2002 is that the local council had over a hundred planning applications for extensions to bed-and-breakfasts in the town, and every one of them cited the garden as the reason.

'The Alnwick Garden is on the main road to Edinburgh, so my challenge is to make sure that people stop off in the area and see what's on offer here. We had well over 300,000 people in our first year, and I'm confident we can beat this.

'I'd have been stuck without our volunteers from the local community, and without all the students from various horticultural colleges on work placement here. Initially, outsiders referred to this place as "the Duchess's Garden", which was completely the opposite of what I was trying to achieve. The helpers got rid of all that, because they rightly felt it was their garden and they took a huge pride in it. They still do, because the whole thing is a great big community project.'

For more information about The Alnwick Garden telephone 01665 511 350, or visit www.alnwickgarden.com

MARYLYN ABBOTT

When Marylyn Abbott, owner of Kennerton Green, Australia's most-visited garden, took a long lease on West Green House in Hampshire, she breathed new life into its long-neglected grounds. Annual replanting, ongoing restoration, and new hard-landscaping projects make it a place to visit year after year.

'My mother and my grandmother had fabulous gardens in New South Wales, and I grew up with a basic understanding of plants – though there weren't many nurseries there and choices were limited.

'The landscape gardens I saw when I first started coming here as a teenager were marvellous, but they were beyond my comprehension because they were so grand, with great sweeping lawns and massive lakes.

'Like any good tourist, I later went to Versailles and Vaux-le-Vicomte, but the biggest influence in my life was Villandry. It was magic so far as I was concerned. That's when I stopped just liking gardens. I would go to the Chelsea Flower Show whenever possible, then take a holiday wandering around the countryside. All I knew about English gardening was of the "ooh" and "aah" variety. They're so beautiful, and you can grow a whole range of the really pretty plants that just can't be grown in Australia.

'Perennials there are a worry, because by the time the flowers are opening, the heat is really intense. Suddenly there'll be two days of scorching winds and the plants just fry. I might get a reasonable display perhaps one year in three. Visually, hot colours fight against the sun, so I usually opt for cooler shades: clear yellows and blues, soft lavenders and white.

'Late in the season at West Green with the cooler climate, everything becomes very exciting. Because of the softer light, I can incorporate strong jewel-like colours such as ruby and amethyst. There's none of this planting an herbaceous border and leaving it to go on forever, which seems accepted practice in England. Each spring we practically pull our beds apart to replant the colour combinations and redefine our shapes and textures.

'We take a different theme for the potager, too. We've done oriental herbs and vegetables, we recreated a Medieval garden, a Middle European one, and we've grown medicinal plants and foodstuffs from the American prairies. Silchester, the Roman ruin, is just up the road, and from what archaeologists have found in the middens we know a lot about the plants people used then, so we're going to put in a Roman garden. I've recently been talking to a white witch, so we're also planting up the woodland as a magic garden. We bust ourselves to tell a whole new story from start to finish within a single season.

'When I first walked round West Green, the soil was dead and much of the garden was derelict: trees had fallen down, hedges had disappeared – it was a mammoth task. After restoring the decorative features, replanting the allées and walkways in yew and box, and using shrubs to pull them all together, it has taken on a life of its own. And since I have a very low boredom tolerance, there's a lot more planned for the future…

For more information about West Green House Garden telephone 01252 845 582. Open from late April to August.

MICHELE OSBORNE

Trained as a linguist, Michèle Osborne of Panorama Landscape Design was commissioned, almost by chance, to design a roof garden in 1984, since when she has collaborated with many leading architects to create astounding outdoor spaces all around the capital and far beyond. New residential developments have become a speciality.

'Roof gardens have become an amazing sales point because city dwellers want to see things from above. So many tall buildings have appeared in recent years and lots of exciting outdoor spaces have been created. The art of landscape gardening has really exploded, not only up in the air, but down on the ground. I love such developments – they involve a radical approach, moving things along stylistically, getting things done efficiently, and using high-specification materials.

'When prospective buyers arrive, they have to look around and be amazed; my brief is always to come up with the "wow factor". This has a lot to do with water. Water features have acquired a bad name through over-use, but the professional article can be truly spectacular. Long rills work well, as do fountains reinterpreted using modern materials such as stainless-steel bowls in tiers, even great overflowing Versailles tubs. We're using the language of the formal garden but in a new context.

'Mosaic is ideal too, because there is often a wall that has to be masked. By the same token, purpose-made trellis can be very beautiful. The real secret is to use good-quality, well-crafted materials, and to work on a big, big scale. Everything should be large and dramatic.

'The new hard-landscaping products that have been developed have banished the once-ubiquitous concrete paviour. Resin-bound gravel is a great favourite of mine: you can dress it simply and it doesn't require maintenance. Or there are exquisite limestones which have appeared from China and India, and I'm also partial to the versatility of concrete.

'For private balconies and roof gardens, decking is still the clients' choice. It works well with modern buildings, but to my mind decking mediated with stone gives a more integrated look. Cedar and iroko are perhaps the best-known timbers, but new woods like ipé and bala have also appeared on the market.

'The most exciting future development is the greening of roofs. Ecologically friendly roofs are already big in Germany and they're taking off in America. These systems use expanded slate, acting as insulation and as a heat reflector. The greenery also cools the city down and re-uses water, creating a whole ecosystem.

For more information about Michèle Osborne's work telephone 020 7703 1704, or visit www.panoramalandscapes.com

PAMELA WOODS

Besides creating public and private gardens with a spiritual focus, Pamela Woods also lectures, writes and holds training workshops on the subject.

'I trained in design at the English Gardening School after completing a botany degree and then spent two or three years in a wonderful euphoric state creating gorgeous Jekyll-like and traditional British gardens. After a while it became apparent that this wasn't hitting the spot for me, and though I was having a great deal of success I realized that something else just had to happen.

'What I did eventually was to sell my home and set off travelling around the world – not really knowing why, or what I was looking for. I'd never had the freedom or opportunity for anything like that before; I just wanted to expand my horizons.

'I went to Sikkim in Northern India, which had just opened up to visitors, and we were taken to some amazing places – right up into the foothills of the Himalayas to see the footprints of snow leopards. And I saw some extraordinary sacred places in Thailand, Malaysia and Bali. From there I went to Australia to visit my sister, then bought myself a camper van and took off on a big outback tour on my own, travelling up towards the centre of the continent. I still wasn't really aware of what I was doing or why I was doing it, but by the time I found myself in the very centre, at Ayer's Rock, or Uluru – which means "belly of the mother" – something happened to me that had never happened in any of the temples or holy sites I'd visited before. In essence, the earth itself is sacred to the Aboriginal people. This experience is at the core of my own spirituality, which is that the earth itself and nature itself is god, everything we need to know.

'Inevitably, this realization had a huge impact on my work when I returned to the UK and I had to carve out a living. I went back to making gardens but I realized there was so much more to making a space on earth than I had been doing previously – although I still think that the simple creation of beauty is a sacred thing. I decided that I was going to design what I called sacred gardens. To begin with I didn't talk directly about what I was doing with my mainstream clients, although perhaps two or three people a year asked me to create this kind of environment. As time moved on, and certainly after I'd done the Feng Shui Garden at Hampton Court Flower Show and received a Silver Gilt medal, it became clear that this would be my whole approach.

We all need a time and a place where we can stop and be still. It's a thread running through so many traditions around the world. Through contemplation we are able to resolve many of the problems in our lives, just by going deeper into ourselves, into that place of stillness. And the garden can be that. The garden has it.

For more information about Pamela Woods' work telephone 01453 885 903, or visit www.sacredgardens.co.uk

PHILIP CAVE

Philip Cave Associates creates gardens worldwide for hotels, shopping centres, airports, hospitals and office blocks. The company also works on large-scale public realm projects and in the domestic sector too, so embraces the entire spectrum of design. Underpinning all these projects is an ethos that springs from director Philip Cave's training in Japanese techniques and aesthetics.

'Any landscape, any garden area – even a car park outside a supermarket – can be made into a place of interest, can be transformed into something original, inventive and innovative. As a practice we aim to raise the profile of a space in order to make it really memorable.

'There has to be structure, there has to be form. A good garden is more than the sum of its parts – when you leave it you should feel as though you've been changed in some way.

'People are drawn to the serenity of Japanese gardens. We are all conscious of leading a stressful life and anything which can help alleviate that is very welcome. A Japanese garden creates a strong sense of stillness, calm and serenity in a very small space, right in the middle of the city.

'One aspect of the Japanese approach is to take the essence of wild nature and bring that into the garden. This is done in a similar way to an artist painting a picture. They'll absorb a scene, distil it to the bare essentials, then recreate it in miniature on canvas. It won't be a direct copy, it will be their interpretation of reality. Designers can bring all this into the urban environment; when people look at their work they are transported back to nature.

'The materials used are always natural, which complements the minimal approach to modern design. Rocks, cobbles and timber create an atmosphere that artificial materials lack. In fact, hard landscaping and the design approach are more significant than the artefacts such as lanterns and water basins that you often find decorating Japanese gardens.

'When I lived in Japan I worked for several eminent designers, culminating in my being taken under the wing of a professor of garden design, who was also a master of the tea ceremony. The tea garden is a wonderful example of various compartments, garden rooms really, all carefully manipulated to create a certain effect. The cares of the world are left behind and thoughts focus on aesthetic and spiritual values. There's a huge tradition there that we can pick up on and translate to great advantage in the West.'

For more information about Philip Cave's work telephone 020 7829 8340 or visit www.philipcave.com

PIPPA GREENWOOD

Gardening author, broadcaster and columnist Pippa Greenwood read Botany at Durham University, took an MSc in Crop Rotation at Reading and then spent 11 years as a distinguished plant pathologist for the RHS at Wisley. She now lives in rural Hampshire, where her young children are hard at work on their own gardening ABCs.

'Gardening is very important for children. If nothing else it gets them out in the open air. Luckily, my two kids have always liked it. I don't know what I would have done with them if they didn't – I suppose I would have made them like it. I reckon that most kids who are a bit noxious are that way because they don't get enough fresh air and exercise – they're not worn out enough.

'Through gardening, children learn to respect their environment, and I think that's really important in the long term. Whether they're watching an earthworm make a worm cast or finding one of those wonderful little bags that a spider weaves to hatch its young in, I think it's lovely for them to have a feel for nature. As adults they'll then be less inclined to run away from spiders and do all those silly things that people do.

'Once you get a child interested in gardening it tends to stay with them. I spent a lot of time with my mother in the garden when I was young and I'm sure that's why I can't get away from the outdoors now. I don't want to get away from it, I expect to be there, I love it.

'The act of gardening helps breed respect for the garden. Once children have grown and nurtured plants themselves they're more inclined to care about them, and to try and avoid injuring them when playing. Obviously, the odd thing is still going to get stamped on and squashed, or have a football or two land on it – but you certainly won't find them jumping up and down on them intentionally as I've seen other people's children do. Also, if your children won't eat things that are good for them, you'll be surprised at what they'll eat if they've grown it themselves.

'Gardening is an incredibly pleasurable activity all round. Children love growing things and, whether they realize it or not, they learn an awful lot in the process. It's education in a wonderfully hidden and interesting way. They can watch seeds germinating, they can see how plants take up water and, if there's an oversight, they find out what happens if you don't water them enough. In the case of things like tomatoes, aubergines or peppers, children can actually see the fruit forming, and before you know it, you've started discovering pollination and all those sorts of things. You can also get into human reproduction – once you go from one, in my experience, you have to cover the other.

'Above all else, once children are used to gardening, you're never going to end up with one of those desperately sad situations where they ask where peas come from after seeing a picture on a packet from the freezer. They'll have seen plants growing; they'll have watched bees about their work so they'll know better than to stamp on them at picnics; they'll have understood how seeds are formed. For me and my family, gardening is an integral part of life – and it's extremely good fun too.'

STEPHEN WOODHAMS

Stephen Woodhams is an innovative floral and landscape designer who has won numerous awards for his gardens at the Chelsea Flower Show. With shops at the prestigious No 1 Aldwych and in Elizabeth Street, Mayfair, a series of high-profile commissions to the credit of his landscape practice, and as the author of several highly successful books, he is a passionate advocate of practical training and, above all else, of teamwork.

'I've been involved with the Chelsea Flower Show ever since I was a student at Wisley, whether simply dressing a conservatory or designing an entire show garden. On a personal level it has been a hugely gratifying experience; on a professional level it has also been a great platform for Woodhams as a business.

'I enrolled on the RHS diploma at the age of sixteen, and I think it is a fantastic stepping-stone for anyone intent on making a career out of gardening. The RHS is a great institution with a huge following, and there is a wonderful collection of people behind the scenes.

'I worked in the herbaceous border during April, May and June – the best time of the year, when everything is really coming to life. I worked in maintenance, and in arboriculture, climbing right into the trees for tree surgery. I also did three months in the fruit garden – and when you have spent six weeks up a ladder pruning hundreds of apple trees in minus-whatever conditions, I can tell you that you never forget how to prune them. The experiences were invaluable.

'On completing my training, I worked for a London company involved in interior as well as exterior landscaping. The year I was there they put an interior landscape into the marquee at Chelsea, with leather sofas around a pool – the judges couldn't believe it! I've always been incredibly fortunate in working with people who were making waves.

'At Woodhams, our aim is to create a seamless line between the inside and the outside. A flooring treatment, for example, can use a single sweep of limestone from the sitting room to the terrace. That of course is a high-end material, but we cover all aspects of the market, and one of the cheapest "stone" floors you can put down is council-grey concrete paving slabs. If they're indoors in a conservatory and outdoors in the garden, the dynamism is still there. It is all about redefining the boundaries of your available space.

'Although the minimal, clean look will always be with us, people want to spice it up a bit now, and I think we're about to go through a big colour phase – with strong palettes in plants as well as in materials. At Woodhams we've already taken our signature galvanized metal containers a stage further with a range of vibrant powder coatings. We've also been doing a lot of English-country-style gardens – with a tweak, of course.

'When I started the business off I never imagined we could do all we have. It's simply because of a brilliant team. You're only as good as they are. That's why you've got to keep putting energy back in to the team so that as the team grows, the business will grow too.

For more information about Stephen Woodhams' work telephone 020 7346 5656, or visit www.woodhams.co.uk

USEFUL CONTACTS

Arboricultural Association
Ampfield House, Romsey, Hampshire SO51 9PA
01794 368 717 www.trees.org.uk

The Building Centre
26 Store Street, London WC1E 7BT
020 7692 4000 www.buildingcentre.co.uk

Capel Manor College
Bullsmoor Lane, Enfield, Middlesex EN1 4RQ
020 8366 4442 www.capel.ac.uk

The English Gardening School
66 Royal Hospital Road, Chelsea, London SW3 4HS
020 7352 4347 www.englishgardeningschool.co.uk

English Heritage
23 Savile Row, London W1S 2ET
020 7973 3000 www.english-heritage.org.uk

Greenmount College
22 Greenmount Road, Antrim, County Antrim BT41 4PU
028 9442 6601 www.greenmount.ac.uk

Henry Doubleday Research Association
Ryton Organic Gardens, Coventry, Warwickshire CV8 3LG
024 7630 3517 www.hdra.org.uk

Inchbald School of Design
32 Eccleston Square, London SW1V 1PB
020 7630 9011 www.inchbald.co.uk

Merrist Wood College
Worplesdon, Surrey GU3 3PE
01483 884 040 www.merristwood.ac.uk

The National Gardens Scheme
Hatchlands Park, East Clandon, Guildford, Surrey GU4 7RT
01483 211 535 www.ngs.org.uk

National Trust
36 Queen Anne's Gate, London SW1H 9AS
020 7222 9251 www.nationaltrust.org.uk

National Trust for Scotland
28 Charlotte Square, Edinburgh EH2 4ET
0131 243 9300 www.nts.org.uk

Pershore College
Pershore, Worcestershire WR10 3JP
01386 552 443 www.pershore.ac.uk

Royal Botanic Gardens, Kew
Richmond , Surrey TW9 3AB
020 8332 5000 www.rbgkew.org.uk

Royal Horticultural Society
80 Vincent Square, London SW1P 2PE
020 7834 4333 www.rhs.org.uk

Scottish Agricultural College
Auchincruive, Ayr KA6 5HW
0800 269 453 www.sac.ac.uk

Society of Garden Designers
Katepwa House, Ashfield Park Avenue, Ross-on-Wye, Herefordshire HR9 5AX
01989 566 695 www.society-of-garden-designers.co.uk

Soil Association
Bristol House, 40–56 Victoria Street, Bristol BS1 6BY
0117 914 2446 www.soilassociation.org

Thrive
The Geoffrey Udall Centre, Beech Hill, Reading RG7 2AT
0118 988 5688 www.thrive.org.uk

Writtle College
Chelmsford, Essex CM1 3RR
01245 424 200 www.writtle.ac.uk

DAVID HARBER SUNDIALS NE
STUBBINGS THE GARDEN SHO
MAGGY HOWARTH OTTER WR
FAIRWEATHER SCULPTURE NI
THE ORKNEY STONE COMPAN
OVER THE GARDEN WALL INDI
DONAGHADEE GARDEN CENT
THE KITCHEN GARDEN JOHN
PENNINE PLAYGROUNDS THE
THE LANDSCAPE ORNAMENT
CENTRE FOR ALTERNATIVE TE
SCOTTS OF THRAPSTON KING
ARCHITECTURAL ANTIQUES S

L WILKIN THE GARDEN STORE
P JASON GRIFFITHS BAILEYS
OUGHT IRON PATIO PLANTING
EL BRIDGES KATHY DALWOOD
SERENA DE LA HEY HORTUS
N OCEAN TRADING COMPANY
RE THE BIG PARK TOM CLARK
ULLEN LIGHTING JARDINIQUE
POTTING SHED URBIS DESIGN
OMPANY

DIRECTORY

LASSCO
HNOLOGY JACQUELINE EDGE
DOVECOTES REDWOOD STONE
OLID SOUL FURNITURE DESIGN

DIRECTORY

SOUTH-EAST ENGLAND

Andrew Crace
Bourne Lane, Much Hadham, Hertfordshire SG10 6ER
01279 842 685 www.andrewcrace.com

Anthony de Grey Trellises
Broadhinton Yard, 77a North Street, London SW4 0HQ
020 7738 8866 www.anthonydegrey.com

Belinda Eade
Studio 70, Great Western Studios, The Lost Goods Building,
Great Western Road, London W9 3NY
020 7266 0328 www.belindaeade.com

Bulbeck Foundry
Reach Road, Burwell, Cambridgeshire CB5 0AH
01638 743 153 www.bulbeckfoundry.co.ukk

CED
728 London Road, West Thurrock, Grays, Essex RM20 3LU
01708 867 237 www.ced.ltd.uk

Clifton Nurseries
5a Clifton Villas, Little Venice, London W9 2PH
020 7289 6851 www.clifton.co.uk

Columbia Road Market
Columbia Road, London E2 www.columbia-flower-market.freewebspace.com

The Conran Shop
Michelin House, 81 Fulham Road, London SW3 6RD
020 7589 7401 www.conran.com

Cranborne Antiques
Stand No 4a, 113 Portobello Road, London W11 2QB
07785 336 574

The Crooked Garden
57 Tarrant Street, Arundel, West Sussex BN18 9DJ
01903 885 133

David Harber Sundials
Valley Farm, Bix, Henley-on-Thames, Oxfordshire RG9 6BW
01491 576 956 www.davidharbersundials.com

Fairweather Sculpture
Hillside House, Starston, Nr Harleston, Norfolk IP20 9NN
01379 852 266 www.fairweathersculpture.com

Garden Architecture
259 Munster Road, Fulham, London SW6 6BW
020 7385 1020 www.gardenarchitecture.net

Gary Drostle
11 Ennis Road, Plumstead, London SE18 2QR
020 8317 2275 www.drostle.com

Gaze Burvill
Redloh House, The Old Gas Works, 2 Michael Road, London SW6 2AD
020 7471 8500 www.gazeburvill.com

Graham Greener
27 Harbour Street, Whitstable, Kent CT5 1AH
01227 277 100 www.grahamgreener.co.uk

The Hannah Peschar Sculpture Garden
Black and White Cottage, Standon Lane, Ockley, Surrey RH5 5QR
01306 627 269 www.hannahpescharsculpture.com

Heals
196 Tottenham Court Road, London W1T 7LQ
020 7636 1666 www.heals.co.uk

Hortus
26 Blackheath Village, London SE3 9SY
020 8297 9439

Indian Ocean Trading Company
155–163 Balham Hill, Clapham Common, London SW12 9DJ
020 8675 4808 www.indian-ocean.co.uk

Jardinique
Old Park Farm, Kings Hill, Beech, Alton, Hampshire GU34 4AW
01420 560 055 www.jardinique.co.uk

John Cullen Lighting
585 Kings Road, London SW6 2EH
020 7371 5400 www.johncullenlighting.co.uk

Judy Greene's Garden Store
11 Flask Walk, Hampstead, London NW3 1HJ
020 7435 3832

Julian Chichester
Studio S, The Old Imperial Laundry, 71 Warriner Gardens, London SW11 4XW
020 7274 8899 www.julianchichester.com

Kathy Dalwood
165 Victoria Road, London NW6 6TE
020 7372 2677 www.kathydalwood.fsnet.co.uk

King Dovecotes
75 Copthorne Road, Felbridge, East Grinstead, Sussex RH19 2PB
01342 324 159 www.kingdovecotes.co.uk

The Kitchen Garden
Church Lane, Troston, Bury St Edmunds, Suffolk IP31 1EX
01359 268 322 www.kitchen-garden-hens.co.uk

LASSCO
St Michael's Church, Mark Street (off Paul Street), London EC2A 4ER
020 7749 9944 www.lassco.co.uk

Leisure Plan
Silver Street, Stansted Mountfitchet, Essex CM24 8HD
01279 816 001 www.leisureplan.co.uk

Marston & Langinger
192 Ebury Street, London SW1W 8UP
020 7881 5717 www.marston-and-langinger.com

The Modern Garden Company
Millars 3, South Mill Road, Bishops Stortford, Hertfordshire CM23 3DH
01279 653 200 www.moderngarden.co.uk

Otter Wrought Iron
12 Fourth Avenue, Bluebridge, Halstead, Essex CO9 2SY
01787 475 060 www.weathervanes.co.uk

Pots and Pithoi
The Barns, East Street, Turners Hill, West Sussex RH10 4QQ
01342 714 793 www.pots-and-pithoi.co.uk

Purves & Purves
220–4 Tottenham Court Road, London W1T 7QE
020 7580 8223 www.purves.co.uk

R K Alliston
173 New Kings Road, London SW6 4SW
0845 130 5577 www.rkalliston.com

Rayment Wirework
Unit 7, Hoo Farm, Monkton Road, Minster-in-Thanet, Kent CT12 4JB
01843 821 628 www.raymentwire.co.uk

RHS London Flower Shows
Lawrence Hall (Greycoat Street), Lindley Hall (Vincent Square), London SW1
020 7649 1885 www.rhs.org.uk

Sally Anderson (Ceramics) Ltd
Parndon Mill, Harlow, Essex CM20 2HP
01279 420 982 www.sally-anderson.co.uk

Stubbings The Garden Shop
Market Place, Burnham Market, Norfolk PE31 8HF
01328 730 668 www.stubbingsgardenshop.co.uk

The Urban Gardener
18 Market Square, Bromley, Kent BR1 1NA
020 8313 3644

Urbis Design
City Studios, Tyssen Street, London E8 2ND
020 7254 0601 www.urbisdesign.co.uk

William Pye
The Studio, Rear of 31 Bellevue Road, London SW17 7EF
020 8682 2727 www.williampye.com

SOUTH-WEST ENGLAND AND WALES

Architectural Heritage
Taddington Manor, Taddington, Nr Cutsdean, Cheltenham, Gloucestershire GL54 5RY
01386 584 414 www.architectural-heritage.co.uk

The Celtic Garden
Bron Meillion, Tregeiriog, Llangollen LL20 7HT
01691 600 259 www.celticgarden.co.uk

Centre for Alternative Technology
Machynlleth, Powys SY20 9AZ
01654 705 950 www.cat.org.uk

The Children's Cottage Company
The Sanctuary, Shobrooke, Crediton, Devon EX17 1BG
01363 772 061 www.play-houses.com

Derwen Garden Centre
Guilsfield, Nr Welshpool, Powys SY21 9PH
01938 553 015 www.derwengardencentre.co.uk

English Hurdle
Curload, Stoke St Gregory, Taunton, Somerset TA3 6JD
01823 698 418 www.hurdle.co.uk

Garden Art
Wilbur House, Middle Leazes, Stroud, Gloucestershire GL5 1LG
01453 756 361 www.gardenart.co.uk

The Garden Store
67 Fore Street, Salcombe, Devon TQ8 8BU
01548 844 449

Jacqueline Edge
The Old Barns, Manor Farm, Chilmark, Wiltshire SP3 5AF
01722 717 800 www.jacquelineedge.com

Jason Griffiths
PO Box 9, Totnes, Devon TQ9 5FN
07971 921 676

Jon Fox Garden Antiques
High Street, Moreton-in-Marsh, Gloucestershire GL5 0AD
01608 650 714/325

Jonathan Garratt
Hare Lane Pottery, Cranborne, Nr Wimborne, Dorset BH21 5QT
01725 517 700 jonathan.garratt@talk21.com

The Landscape Ornament Company
Long Barn, Patney, Devizes, Wiltshire SN10 3RB
01380 840 533 www.landscapeornament.com info@landscapeornament.com

---

Natural Driftwood Sculptures
Sunburst House, Elliot Road, Bournemouth BH11 8LT
01202 578 274 www.driftwoodsculptures.co.uk enquiries@driftwoodsculptures.co.uk

---

Neil Wilkin
Unit 3, Wallbridge Business Park, Frome, Somerset BA11 5JY
01373 452 574 www.neilwilkin.com neil@neilwilkin.com

The Potting Shed
Market Place, High Street, Castle Cary, Somerset BA7 7AL
01963 350 555

Redwood Stone
The Stoneworks, West Horrington, Wells, Somerset BA5 3EH
01749 677 777 www.redwoodstone.com mail@redwoodstone.com

Serena de la Hey
The Willows, Curload, Stoke St Gregory, Taunton, Somerset TA3 6JD
01823 698 049 www.serenadelahey.com info@serenadelahey.com

The Smack Iron Company
The Old Forge, The Old Potato Yard, Manor Farm, Lydeway, Wiltshire SN10 3PU
07966 495 561

SureSet UK
Unit 32, Deverill Road Trading Estate, Sutton Veny, Warminster, Wiltshire BA12 7BZ
01985 841 180 www.sureset.co.uk

Tom Clark
Hurst Barton Studio, Hurst, Martock, Somerset TA12 6JU
01935 822 833

The Wadham Trading Company
France House, Digbeth Street, Stow-on-the-Wold, Gloucestershire GL54 1BN
01451 830 308 www.wadhamtrading.co.uk

MIDLANDS

Access Irrigation
Crick, Northampton NN6 7XS
01788 823 811 www.access-irrigation.co.uk

Baileys
The Engine Shed, Station Approach, Ross-on-Wye, Herefordshire HR9 7BW
01989 563 015 www.baileyshomeandgarden.com

E H Thorne (Beehives) Ltd
Beehive Works, Wragby, Market Rasen, Lincolnshire LN8 5LA
01673 858 555 www.thorne.co.uk

Garden Images
15 Meer Street, Stratford-upon-Avon, Warwickshire CV37 6QB
0845 130 4321 www.garden-images.co.uk

Haddonstone
The Forge House, East Haddon, Northampton NN6 8DB
01604 770 711 www.haddonstone.co.uk

Holloways
Lower Court, Suckley, Worcestershire WR6 5DE
01886 884 665 www.holloways.co.uk

Juro Antiques
Whitbourne, Worcester WR6 5SF
01886 821 261 www.juro.co.uk

Mark Pedro de la Torre
The Courtyard, Old Rectory, Stoke Lacy, Herefordshire HR7 4HH
01432 820 500

Michael Hill
Cressy Hall, Gosberton, Spalding, Lincolnshire PE11 4JD
01775 840 925

Patio Planting
Cobb Hall Yard, St Paul's Lane, Lincoln LN1 3AX
01522 536 573

Raffles Thatched Garden Buildings
Church Farm, Main Street, Overseal, Derbyshire DE12 6LG
01283 762 469 www.rafflesgb.com

Scotts of Thrapston
Bridge Street, Thrapston, Northamptonshire NN14 4LR
01832 732 366 www.scottsofthrapston.co.uk

Stephen McRae
Wood House, Staplow, Ledbury, Herefordshire HR8 1NP
01531 640 051

Whichford Pottery
Whichford, Nr Shipston-on-Stour, Warwickshire CV36 5PG
01608 684 416 www.whichfordpottery.com

NORTH OF ENGLAND AND NORTHERN IRELAND

Andy Thornton Architectural Antiques
Victoria Mills, Stainland Road, Greetland, Halifax, West Yorkshire HX4 8AD
01422 377 314 www.ataa.co.uk

Donaghadee Garden Centre
34 Stockbridge Road, Donaghadee, County Down BT21 0PN
028 9188 3603

Errington Reay & Co. Ltd
Bardon Mill, Hexham, Northumberland NE47 7HU
01434 344 245 www.erringtonreay.co.uk

Havenplan
The Old Station, Station Road, Killamarsh, Sheffield, Yorkshire S21 8EN
0114 248 9972

The Iron Design Company
8 Royal Parade, Harrogate, North Yorkshire HG1 2SZ
01423 538 725 www.irondesign.co.uk

Jenni Walker's Potting Shed
6 Montpellier Mews, Harrogate, North Yorkshire HG1 2TQ
01423 526 988

The Landscape Centre
24 Donegore Hill, Dunadry, Antrim BT41 2QU
028 9443 2175 www.landscapecentre.net

Maggy Howarth
Cobblestone Designs, Hilltop, Wennington, Lancaster LA2 8NY
01524 274 264 www.maggyhowarth.co.uk

Over the Garden Wall
93 Commercial Street, Norton, Malton, North Yorkshire YO17 9HY
01653 698 880 www.overthegardenwall.com

Pennine Playgrounds
Waterside Business Park, Keighley Road, Silsden, West Yorkshire BD20 0EA
01535 656 500 www.pennine-playgrounds.co.uk

Plants of Special Interest
4 High Street, Braithwell, Nr Rotherham, South Yorkshire S66 7AL
01709 790 642 www.psinursery.co.uk

The Potting Shed
13 London Road, Alderley Edge, Cheshire SK9 7JT
01625 585 819

Richard Charters
Biteabout Farm, Lowick, Berwick-upon-Tweed, Northumberland TD15 2QE
01289 388 273

Solid Soul Furniture Design
High Hazel Hall, Clapham, Lancaster LA2 8HN
01524 251 500 www.solidsoul.moonfruit.com

Stapeley Water Gardens
Stapeley, Nantwich, Cheshire CW5 7LH
01270 623 868 www.stapeleywatergardens.com

SCOTLAND

The Big Park
73 Dublin Street, Newtown, Edinburgh EH3 6NS
0131 558 9360 www.thebigpark.com

Catriona McLean
Sanquhar House, Sanquhar, Dumfriesshire DG4 6JL
01659 50282 www.catrionamclean.com

Iain McGregor Designs
Greenbank, West End, Gordon, Berwickshire TD3 6JP
01573 410 277

Louise Kerr
1/2 of 10 Peinchorran, Braes, by Portree, Isle of Skye IV51 9LL
01478 650 338

Nigel Bridges
No 1 Cottage, Magdalenehall Farm, St Boswells, Melrose, TD6 0EB
01835 822 818 www.nigelbridges.com

The Orkney Stone Company
Viewfield, Church Road, South Ronaldsay, Orkney KW17 2SR
01856 831 462 www.orkneystone.com

Pear Tree
The Stables, Maunsheugh Road, Fenwick, Ayrshire KA3 6AN
01560 600 111 www.peartreehouse.com

ACKNOWLEDGEMENTS

The author would like to thank:
Jacque Acaster; Sharon Amos; Neil Andrews; Veronique Baxter; Matt Bell; Daniela Bernadelle; Liz Boyd; Martin Breese; Brigitte Bunnell; Anna Buxton; Richard Cassy; Susan Cassy; Emma Clegg; Guy Cooper; Katey Day; Barry Delves; Lorraine Dickey; Michael Ellison; Jude Evans; Antoinette Galbraith; Sophie Gibson; Nabil Abou-Hamad; Orlando Hamilton; Vickie Hamilton; Jane Healing; Karen Higgs; Anne-Marie Hoines; Martin Hunka; Ann Jaye; Michael Johnson; Roger Katz; Angela Kingdon; Benois von Kitting; Chi Lam; Heidi Lascelles; Rob Linley; Sybella Marlow; Steve McCarthy; Ann Mollo; Ailsa Murray; Geraldine Murray; Mum and Dad; Anthony Noel; Michèle Osborne; Mike Park; Christopher Parry; James Phillips; Gareth Pottle; Antoinette Putnam; Jilliana Ranicar-Breese; Anke Reichelt; Anne Robbins; Beth Robson; Diana Ross; Marie Saba; Karin Scherer; Valerie Scriven; Jane Seabrook; Liz Seeber; Stephen Simpson; Ian Smith; Catharine Snow; Shane Sorenson; Gill Soulsby; Ruth Swindon; Gordon Taylor; Elspeth Thompson; Lauretta Tomlinson; Kath Tudball; Tom Vach; Diana Vowles; Kit Webster; Julia Woollams; Sharon Wright; Maureen Zakaria; and Zak Zakaria.

Conran Octopus would like to thank all contributing shops, garden designers and the following manufacturers and photographers for their kind permission to reproduce their images in this book.

2 IOTA; 12 Andrew Crace; 14–15 Anthony de Grey Trellises Ltd; 23 Jo Reid & John Peck; 24–25 Matthew Bell; 26 The Conran Shop; 28 Deborah Cutler/ Cranbourne Antiques; 30 Bill Philip; 32 Bruce Harber; 34 David Fairweather; 36–37 Steve Wooster; 40–41 Peter Knab; 45 Industrial Fragment by Rick Kirby/The Hannah Peschar Sculpture Garden designed by Anthony Paul; 48 IOTA; 60 Richard Valencia; 62 David King; 64–65 Charlie Colmer; 66 Lassco; 70–71 Marston & Langinger Ltd; 76 Pots & Pithoi; 81 RK Alliston; 84 RHS; 90 Jacqueline Walker; 94 Michael Baister; 95 Peter Anderson; 100 Creativity Jones; 102–103 Centre for Alternative Technology; 107 Dingley Dell Enterprises; 112–113 Lorna Yabsley; 116–117 Steve Bond; 120–121 Jonathan Garratt; 122–123 The Landscape Ornament Company; 124–125 Magnus Harding; 128 Clare Cooke; 130–131 Tim Mercer; 132 Bill de la Hey; 134–135 Sefton Whorlow; 138 John Davies; 146–147 Mark Bailey; 150 Courtesy of Garden Images; 154–155 Haddonstone Ltd; 158 Mark de la Torre; 159 Mark de la Torre (Designer: Andy Sturgeon, Chelsea 2001); 165 Raffles; 166–167 Scotts of Thrapston; 170 Courtesy of Whichford Pottery; 174–175 Courtesy of Andy Thornton; 176–177 Alexander Rose Ltd; 184–185 Catriona McLean; 188–189 Val Corbett; 190–191 Stewart Pote; 198 Angie & Paul Boyer/Craftsman Magazine; 202 Stapeley Water Gardens Ltd; 216 Louise Scott; 217 Theories Landscapes; 218–219 Pear Tree; 225 Lowell Georgia/Corbis; 226–227 Mr Ian Fraser-Martin (Sculptor: Angela Conner); 228 Andrew Lawson (Designer: Anthony Noel); 230 Andrew Lawson (Designer: Arabella Lennox-Boyd); 233 Andrew Lawson (Designers: Piet Oudolf & Arne Maynard, RHS Chelsea 2000); 234 Ariel Skelley/Corbis; 237 Fhuji Kobayashi/Stone/Getty Images; 238 Bill Burlington; 242 Clive Boursnell; 245 Graeme Peacock; 246 Clay Perry; 248–249 Marianne Majerus (Designer: Michèle Osborne); 250 John Glover (Sculptor: Simon Packard/Garden Art); 252–253 Philip Cave; 254 Ariel Skelley/Corbis

The author has made every effort to ensure that the information contained in this book is correct and up to date at the time of publication. He apologizes in advance for any unintentional omissions and would be pleased to include updated information in subsequent editions.